Tales for Jung Folk

Books by Richard Roberts

TAROT AND YOU (1971, 1984)

TAROT REVELATIONS (1981) with Joseph Campbell

Tales for Jung Folk

ORIGINAL FAIRYTALES FOR PERSONS OF ALL AGES DRAMATIZING C.G. JUNG'S ARCHETYPES OF THE COLLECTIVE UNCONSCIOUS

by

Richard Roberts

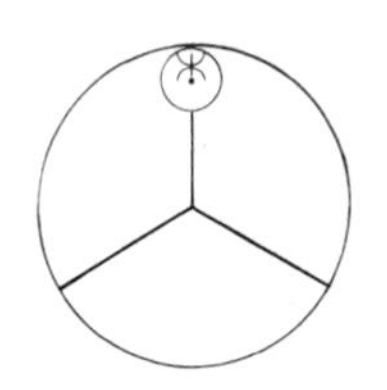

VERNAL EQUINOX PRESS
BOX 581
SAN ANSELMO, CA 94960

FIRST EDITION

INTERNATIONAL STANDARD BOOK NUMBERS:
0-942380-01-0 (paperback)
0-942380-02-9 (hard cover)

LIBRARY OF CONGRESS CATALOG CARD NUMBER: 83-40049

Grateful acknowledgement is made to Princeton University Press for permission to quote from the *Collected Works of C. G. Jung* and to Doubleday and Co. for a quote from *Man and His Symbols.*

Typesetting in Baskerville Roman by Archetype, Berkeley, CA.

CONTENTS

ILLUSTRATIONS

To C. G. Jung, his ghost and his living spirit.

To Joseph Campbell, who gave me C. G. Jung, and who has guided me like the Self.

To my mother and father, who read to me my first fairytales before I could read.

INTRODUCTION

Our title contains a pun. Jung is pronounced "Yung" in Swisser-Deutsch. *Tales for Jung Folk* has a very odd history indeed. In 1973 I began to have some very interesting dreams that I found I could complete upon awakening by the "active imagination" process. Creative imagination, of course, is nurtured far more in artistic persons than in the average man, who does not know how to utilize it. The mechanic would not throw away his tools, the draftsman his board and T-square, and the manual laborer would do nothing to harm his meal-ticket, his own body. Similarly an artist would never toss out a valuable dream upon awakening. For an artist—whether painter, writer, or musician—recognizes imagination to be the wellspring, the very origin, of what he creates, whether it be a painting, a play, or a song. So in sleeping, creative persons are unconsciously alert—if I may use a paradoxical phrase—to the creative potentiality of a dream. Thus while asleep a dramatist may watch a play, as a spectator in the dream's audience; a sculptor may see a form he has never seen in life and "remember" it from the dream; a painter may see an image or a combination of colors that will inspire him to put it on canvas; and a song-writer may hear the notes and lyric in his head while dreaming. All of this inspiration occurs in what I call the Dream Castle, or the unconscious mind, described in the first tale.

To his undying credit, Jung was the first psychologist to regard the unconscious as more than a mine for clues to neurotic symptoms, as in psychoanalysis generally, or as a source of unending nightly nonsense—the lay attitude towards dreams. Indeed, Jung restored to the unconscious and to the dream the spiritual status that it had in such great traditions as Egypt at the time of the pyramids, or Greece of the dream-diviners and soothsayers. These ancient priests and priestesses were our first psychologists, for they interpreted dreams, and the entire community's well-being depended upon what they saw, whether for good or ill.

Throughout history, those cultures which have revered the dream have attained the highest spiritual development, as in Egypt and Greece. Later in Renaissance Europe, the same spiritual tradition was to surface again, disguised as a chemical process for transmuting lead; whereas in reality the gross lead transformed into gold was no less than the consciousness of the alchemist and his *soror*, the crucial feminine partner in the process. More probably there was no "wife" involved, she being symbolic of the feminine unconscious, counterpart to masculine, rational consciousness. Or even more likely, as Jung has pointed out in his three monumental works on alchemy, the *soror,* without whom the transformation of consciousness is incomplete, is the *anima,* the feminine "archetype" residing in the male unconscious, bestower of all the psychic qualities that balance rational consciousness.

Any discussion of Jungian psychology is incomplete without mention of the archetypes, which are formless *unconscious quantities* which acquire *conscious qualities* of various forms. According to Jung, "the term 'archetype' is often misunderstood as meaning certain definite mythological images or motifs. But these are nothing more than conscious representations; it would be absurd to assume that such variable representations could be inherited. The archetype is a tendency to form such representations of a motif—representations that can vary a great deal in detail without losing their basic pattern." (Jung, *Man and His Symbols*)

As to the "basic pattern," or form of the archetypes, it "might perhaps be compared to the axial system of a crystal, which, as it were, preforms the crystalline structure in the mother liquid, although it has no material existence of its own. This first appears according to the specific way in which the ions and molecules aggregate. The archetype in itself is empty and purely formal, nothing but . . . a possibility of representation which is given *a priori.* The representations themselves are not inherited, only the forms. . . ."

Thus, the active imagination process is a method whereby the formless archetypes in the "mother liquid" of the unconscious "crystallize," or acquire manifest forms. In *Analytical Psychology: Its Theory and Practice,* Jung states that "active imagination means that the images have a life of their own, and that the symbolic events develop according to their own logic—that is, of course, if your conscious reason does not interfere." Active imagination is a psychic state, therefore, in which conscious and unconscious minds are cooperating fully, as in the alchemical process, to produce the "gold," the images with a "life of their own."

This gold is the *aurum non vulgi,* not the material, common gold, but a psychic gold, the images that are the fount, as I said before, of all arts for the creative person. The active imagination process is valuable for all readers, whether or not they are creative, because it enables the archetypes to come through from the unconscious and make themselves known to consciousness. I use the word *them* to describe the archetypes because they behave exactly like persons, possessing a psychic life of their own, independent of the conscious mind and the ego *whether or not the conscious mind chooses to recognize them* and accept them into consciousness. Jung's great intuition and contribution to psychology was to delineate the archetypes and to demonstrate in an empirical way precisely how through *projection,* with case studies based upon dream interpretation, the archetypes took over the conscious mind, usurping the ego's proper autonomy, so that these "autonomous complexes," as Jung calls them, piped the tune to consciousness. The implications for a human life are devastating! For at every turn the life is out of control, purposeless, subject to moods, rages, depressions, inflations, so that one's life resembles a tiny ship tossed willy-nilly on the breast of a great ocean. And, indeed, that metaphor is apt for the conscious mind, also frequently described as the tip of an iceberg, and that part of the mind below water—the unconscious—drops down to the unfathomable depths. Whereas, when the ego accepts into partial consciousness the other members of the psychic family, the archetypes, then that unconscious sea works in harmony with the tiny ship of consciousness, which then can sail on a course of higher purpose, aided by unconscious currents. And from those mysterious depths, consciousness may retrieve, untarnished by time, the golden treasures of the Self.

"Who or what are these archetypes?" says the conscious mind, alarmed, if never before having heard such dire threats to its autonomy as I have described (perhaps too poetically for the scientific mind). Well, dear reader, there is for one your *shadow,* repository of all your worst characteristics, swept as it were under the rug of consciousness, only to emerge again in unguarded moments. And when the shadow usurps consciousness, we have the criminal, "into" confrontation, we might say, as a way of life. By contrast, your *Self* will direct your loftiest aspirations, fulfilling—if selfhood is attained—your spiritual potential. And your most ecstatic moments in life—when you are in love—will come from the archetypes of *animus* or *anima.* So you see, the archetypes are not to be feared, but to be welcomed by the conscious mind; therefore, the method of active imagination (along with dream recall and dream analysis) is the best method for bringing the archetypes to the surface of consciousness, in order to live in harmony with them.

Many years ago, while teaching a course in Robert Frost to college sophomores, I had a dream that the text of Frost poems was open before me, and one particularly struck my fancy because I could not recall having seen it before. I read it several times, and then in that rare state of cooperation that can occur with consciousness in the dream, I thought, "Well, if the poem is not one of Frost's, despite its being here in his collected works, I shall memorize it and have it for my own when I awaken." Whereupon, I read it several times, awakened, and wrote it down verbatim, the result of which you see below.

I had thought that something rocky
    Would stand against the sea,
But wave on wave brought the land down,
    Cliff and dune tumbled in,
    Sand and rubble showered me,
    Surely all would fall to sea.

I had thought the scene empty,
    Yet something glinted sun—
The fragile nets of five fishermen.
    Casting when waters outrun,
    Letting surf swirl nets in,
They catch a rhythm of life—and men.

Today I stand in the throat of the sea,
    Watching waves work for them,
    But what when man is alone,
And sea strives but to drag him in?
"Are you here always?" I call to them.
    "Always, always," say the men.

Now the fascinating thing about this poem is that it symbolically (and quite unconsciously, since I was asleep at the time) describes the way in which it was created by the unconscious. The first stanza presents consciousness as land, a shoreline against which the unconscious sea begins to erode. The next stanza presents five fishermen, the five senses, sensation, the other way of perception besides intuition. Utilizing the waters of the unconscious, "They catch a rhythm of life—and men." This rhythm, or harmony between the men of the land, the five senses of consciousness, and the waters of the unconscious, retrieves in its net the poem itself! The final stanza presents the ego in the form of the "I" narrator, who fears "when man is alone,/ And sea strives but to drag him in." The ego seeks reassurance that it will not be overwhelmed and calls to the men, "Are you here always?" The answer is reassuring and at the same time ominous, as if these "men," who can stand so easily "in the throat of the sea," were at last not men but the archetypes of the collective unconscious.

My next profound encounter with the unconscious occurred in a dream in which I knew I was very deeply asleep and yet consciously aware. Recognizing this to be the conscious sleep coveted by the mystics, I mentally asked the meaning of all life, and was given a wisdom symbol which is beyond the scope of this book, but which appears in my book *Tarot Revelations* in the chapter "The Caduceus Reading."

And so, having received previously these two treasures from the unconscious, I was not surprised that, while in preparation for a course called "Pathways of Individuation," I began to have dreams in the form of fairytales which were not always complete in the dream state, but which I "finished" in the hypnogogic state between sleep and wakening.

This period in my life when these dreams began to come was particularly enriching because I had just begun the collaboration with Joseph Campbell on *Tarot Revelations,* and new revelations were appearing about the Tarot on almost a daily basis. These revelations were thanks to Joseph Campbell, because at the time he was directing me—almost like a physical manifestation of the Self—on my path of individuation. Particularly rewarding were Jung's three volumes on alchemy which Campbell had given me, and in these I found the alchemical pictures which suggested my theory of the alchemical origins of the twenty-two cards of the Tarot's Major Arcana. In *Tarot and You* (1971) I had presented the correlation of Jung and Tarot (since copied by others without credit to me), utilizing the free-association technique of psychology integrated with an awareness of the Jungian archetypes. Furthermore, I introduced in that volume the Jungian Spread, a mandala-like layout of cards which included positions for the *shadow* and *animus/a,* two inner archetypes which tend to usurp consciousness when not partially integrated. Even today, twelve years later, I still feel that the Jungian Spread is the most valid way to read the cards since it is a microcosm of the pathway of individuation, a reading not just for the particular moment in time when the reading occurs, but a life-reading from birth to death.

As the reader can see, I am interested in whatever methods open a channel for the wisdom of the archetypes of the collective unconscious to come through to consciousness, be it dream, active imagination, or free-associating with Tarot cards. Incidentally, any association of Tarot with the Devil or evil-doing I reject out of hand as products of a superstitious mind. I am interested in psychology, not the occult. Albeit that the human mind does have its dark side, the way to throw light upon it is integration of the dangerous unconscious elements, not by rejecting it as evil and opposing psychoanalysis, as certain religions have done in the name of so-called goodness.

At the same time I was doing my readings in alchemy, Joseph Campbell, who has written on the value of fairytales in *The Flight of the Wild Gander,* was directing me to the von Franz studies, *An Introduction to the Interpretation of Fairy Tales* and *Problems of the Feminine in Fairy Tales,* in which she, as Jung had done, was using examples from fairytales to clarify her analysis of the archetypes. It was then that I realized I might have a potential book, *for each story coming through by active imagination was illustrating a particular archetype.* If the whole family of archetypes would eventually manifest then I would have a publishable volume. Back in the early 1970's I submitted the first tales to Hugh Van Dusen of Harper and Row. He was most encouraging and told me to go ahead and write the other stories, whereupon I had to tell him that I was not writing the stories, they were writing themselves, and only God (or the Self) knew when the next would manifest. Well, this is not the kind of news an editor likes to hear, of course, but Hugh said he would wait lest impatience spoil the pudding.

In the interim, I started my own publishing house, Vernal Equinox Press, from my birthday on March 21st, with *Tarot Revelations* as the first title. The tales took a long time coming—ten years—and except for "The Four Rings," which contains many conscious elements, such as the riddles, are all the product of active imagination. The stories appear in the order in which they came from the unconscious. It is my fondest hope that many of my readers will be stimulated to open their own minds to the unconscious by the active imagination process.

Lastly, in writing these tales I was aware that many of the readers would know nothing of the archetypes, and at the same time, there was available no text on Jungian psychology for either high school or college students. Therefore, a primer was added to each story explaining as simply as possible the marvellous members of the mind's family, the archetypes of the collective unconscious. Jung had once written, "My life has been singularly poor in outward happenings. I cannot tell much about them, for it would strike me as hollow and insubstantial. I can understand myself only in the light of inner happenings. It is these that make up the singularity of my life. . . ."

THE DREAM CASTLE

Once upon a time there was a castle created by a Great Magician to hide a Great Mystery. When people came to the castle they were dreaming, but the secret of the Great Mystery was that when they were dreaming, they were actually awake. And when they were awake, they slept, ever so soundly in the web of illusion known as The World, which the Great Magician had woven.

The Dream Castle was created by the Great Magician at the wedding of Time and Space. If you have a map made before the wedding of Time and Space, you know how to find the castle because sometimes it is in one place and sometimes in another, and sometimes it is in more than one place at once, because it is Nowhere, but Everywhen.

Through all the centuries that time had been piling up dust in the castle, only a very few knew they were awake when they dreamed, and these were The Awakened Ones. Because they were awake they could call on all the dreams of all time, and they could know them and make them their own dreams. And so the Awakened Ones grew as they absorbed all the dreams of their own universes, and then began on the dreams of other universes.

Once upon another time, when one of the Awakened Ones had absorbed all the universal dreams, he would then have the power of the Great Magician and would create a universe himself, and in it he would have his own Dream Castle to hide his own Great Mystery—of course, not the same mystery that the Great Magician had created; for once One Awakens to a mystery it is no longer a mystery and is never used again.

In the castle lived the Dreams. Many were the personal dreams of the Living Dead and the Dying Living. Graves are great places for dreaming. After centuries of flowers and forgetful rains the tiny, inconsequential dreams are washed away and certain Big Dreams remain to be told and retold, sung anew in each spring rain and spun of silver like the web of time, constantly reborn as the dead re-create themselves through the living.

There were so many dreams in the Dream Castle that they could never be counted. As stars in the sky have many worlds, so the countless generations had dreamed on and on—the lifetime dreams of one man on one planet myriad as stars in the sky.

Everyman's dreams were in the castle. They would never be lost or forgotten, only undreamed. If a man wanted to visit a particular dream a million years hence, it would still be there for him, unchanged but changing; for as soon as a dream is dreamed it has its own life and can grow and become Big just like its dreamer. Or so it seemed, for the Great Magician's magic was such that neither dream or dreamer would ever be able to tell whether the dreamer had dreamed the dream, or whether the dream had dreamed the dreamer.

Just as the Dream Castle was the storehouse of Everyman's dream, so too were stored there the dreams of All Time. The dreams of Time were eternal, for Time exists all at once; yet the Great Magician had made men see time as moments that washed over their eyes, ceaseless as the waves of the sea.

The Eternal Dreams of Time were gigantic, their legs stretching out into other dimensions of other worlds, so that they walked a path strewn with stars through a million universes at once, and had something in common with each one, while their arms reached out endlessly in time to other times when the Eternal Dreams were dreaming timelessly. The Wise Old Man—the Ancient of Days—was there, his beard wagging to every windy universe, his staff still supporting him though his spirit had long since given up need of his decrepit frame.

But for anyone in the world, the castle will always be there. Even when the Great Clock of Time has rusted its hands and stopped forever. And even if it is not in the place that you look, it will be in another, or more than one, for each of us has a Big Dream waiting there to awaken those who would become Awakened Ones.

Primer for "The Dream Castle"

Welcome to the Dream Castle, and welcome also to the psychology of Jung. The Dream Castle is a metaphor for the unconscious mind, but it *is* conscious, however, in a paradoxical way, in that it has a purpose and seemingly exerts control over the conscious mind.

Every Castle has a treasure, and the treasure in the Dream Castle, or the unconscious mind, is the dreaming Self. Jung has called the Self, a "God-image." The awareness of the dreaming Self is in reality greater than that of one awake because to be awake is to perceive the world by means of the five senses, and modern biology and physics has taught us that the perceived world is illusionary. For example, the human eye is programed, so-to-speak, by the brain *not* to see certain frequencies of "reality" viewed by the eye. Thus, that reality is never registered by the brain, and it is as if the eye never "saw" that reality.

In teaching us about another order of reality, "The Dream Castle," therefore, is not so much a tale as a parable. In the same way, Jungian psychology does not regard dreams as neurotic symptoms of the disturbed psyche, as in traditional Freudian psychology, but as pathways, adventurous trails, yellow-brick-roads to higher consciousness. In Jungian psychology, dreams have a "meaning" transcending the illness, the disturbed psyche, and even the interpretation of the dream itself. That meaning is that the dream world is itself eternal, being "Everywhen" but "Nowhere," not of space/time's illusionary world of atoms and molecules. Now since the dream world is created by the unconscious mind, which is itself non-material, then can we not imagine that the creator of the dream, the dreaming Self, is eternal also?

When the conscious mind becomes aware of the unconscious mind and knows that it is dreaming, then one is Awakened, a state of unconscious consciousness sought after and cherished in the East, but totally neglected in the West except among proponents of Jungian psychology. Very often we get hints, while in the Dream Castle, about our lives and what to do with them; hence the unconscious *is* conscious, demonstrating that each life has a *particular* purpose, unique for that individual alone. The term Big Dream is used by Jungians to describe dreams so powerful in their impact, so beautiful in effect, that we are left ever after with a sense of awe. Big Dreams occur when the Self in the psyche is creating changes that occur first on the unconscious or inner plane, and then manifest in changes in the life itself. In other words, the old life no longer fits, like an outworn shoe, and a new awareness, and perhaps a complete transformation of consciousness begins to emerge. Thus the importance of writing down these dreams and keeping open a line to the unconscious mind, without which we cannot grow and evolve to the fullest extent of our individual humanity. No other psychological method offers as great a chance for personal evolution as Jungian psychology. By contrast Freudian psychology is inclined to focus not upon the future potential of the individual, but upon the particulars of the past life which contributed to the present illness or unhappiness. This perpetuates the fixation within the family circle. The ultimate goal of Freudian psychology is to fit the individual back into society, functioning as happily as possible. Jungian psychology promulgates discovery, change, and the growth of new consciousness; hence the individual journey is of greater importance than social functioning, even though it may lead to personal confrontations with society.

The clues, therefore, to new psychic growth are taken from the unconscious in the form of the archetypal language of Big Dreams in the Dream Castle. Knowing how to interpret the archetypes of the collective unconscious is important to each one of us in order to know how to trim our sails to the way the psyche's wind is blowing. In other words, if we fight change with great resistance, clinging to traditions that no longer suit us, out of fear or stubborness, the unconscious will be the first to let us know, through the message of the dream, that something is wrong. Another way to discover the role of the unconscious in influencing our lives is to observe the effects of the archetypes in our daily routines, particularly in interpersonal relationships. We may believe that we are functioning consciously, but in reality the archetypes are piping the tune from the unconscious. The ego resists recognition of the archetypes, because it likes to think of itself as the whole show, whereas we are a "family" of unconscious figures (the archetypes) and an aloof ego.

Knowing how the archetypes affect our relationships with others ultimately leads to our acquiring real autonomy in interpersonal situations, so that our emotional needs are met and not neglected. But perhaps the most valuable function of the archetypes is to provide a way of discovering and then living out our personal myth. Ever seeking to fulfill their urge towards conscious expression, the archetypes become manifest to the conscious mind when we permit our creative potentialities full reign; then one has a sense of purpose and fulfillment, the archetypes providing the clear channel from the unconscious to the conscious mind. The following tales will present specific archetypes, depicted in appropriately symbolic garb.

"The Dream Castle" begins this book because no one can gain self-knowledge without first discovering the nature of his own personal unconscious. If one permits his dreams to speak for him, he will discover both his strengths and his inadequacies, the latter being the archetype of the shadow, which we shall explore in the next tale, "Ruckus in the Well." Without renewal from the unconscious well-spring of life, libido energy is attenuated, and we fall into depression. Without awareness of our worst traits we become possessed by them. Knowledge acquired in the Dream Castle, however, may correct an imbalance on the side of consciousness, and set us aright again.

Our dreams are our creations, and, therefore, our responsibility. We must own up to what is in them. They do not just happen to us—we create them as a cooperative act of the archetypal family working through consciousness. So too, the events of our lives *seem* to merely happen, whereas if we can awaken from that illusion, we can see how each daily event is orchestrated by the total psyche, including the unconscious, indeed, even the so-called chance happenings, wherein Jungians recognize the desire of the psyche to *cause* the event to "happen," to which cause and effect they give the name synchronicity.

Dreams possess their own dynamism. Nothing in the universe is static. Once dreamed, a dream changes upon recall, and then transforms itself again when again recalled. The dreamer is changed by the dream, and the dream by the dreamer, so that neither is the same again; for the dream is the unconscious of man, his deathless, universal dimension transcending space and time. A clock can rust its hands and stop, but not time. Time exists *all at once,* open at both ends, without beginning or end. Of course, we could not function in the present if we did not perceive time as a series of moments that "happen" to us, washing over our eyes, "ceaseless as the waves of the sea."

The Big Dreams in the Dream Castle await those who would become Awakened Ones. The Big Dreams awaken us. They tell us that our little lives are part of a greater Life, in which each of us has a role to play in creating the Universe by our Dreaming. The cover illustration for this book, the same illustration facing our next tale, "Ruckus in the Well," depicts two creations, first that of the Great Magician "creating the web of illusion known as the world." The Great Magician is another name for God, Whom we cannot see, since He has hidden himself so cleverly in the Great Mystery He has created, but He manifests also as Father Time, with hourglass and scythe, reaping the days of our lives after "the beginning of creation, reckoned from the moment when Father Time set the cosmic clock to spinning, impelling the stars on their solitary journey across forever."

". . . whoever looks into the mirror of the water will see first of all his own face." —C. G. Jung

RUCKUS IN THE WELL

Once upon a time in a very pleasant little town called Once Was, there lived a little old man at the bottom of a well. Since the well was the source of life-giving water for the entire town, sooner or later during a day, everyone in the town came to the well for a refreshing draught, or to fill a bucket to carry home for bathing or cooking. This was just what the little man liked best, for no one ever stopped at the well without addressing a few polite words of acknowledgment to the little man, who was known simply as Ruckus. Of course, no one could hear his response, since the well was very deep, but they could see him peering up and they knew by his gestures and prancing that he knew they recognized him.

In those days, the well water was crystal clear, probably because its constant use caused the deep spring that fed it to pour in new waters each day.

How long Ruckus had been at the bottom of the well no one could remember. Mrs. Oak, who was the oldest woman in Once Was, could remember her grandmother telling her about Ruckus even as a "tad," as the youngsters of the town were called. Ruckus went back to the beginning of creation, reckoned from the moment when Father Time set the cosmic clock to spinning, impelling the stars on their solitary journey across forever.

Ruckus was the ugliest man who had ever been, but no one seemed to mind very much. "There's a little of Ruckus in everyone," was a saying in the town. Each day when the townspeople came to the well for their water, they always saw in Ruckus something of themselves. If the little boy had stolen from the cook's jampot while her back was turned, he certainly would see jam on Ruckus' fingers. The little girl who had pulled the cat's tail would flounce up to the well sassy as you please, but while she hauled up the bucket, there was Ruckus looking like the nastiest imp that ever lived. No child ever left the well unchastened. "The better for it," as the grownups would say.

But Ruckus was good for them too, as they all knew. The burgher who had charged his neighbor too dearly saw a pantomime at the bottom of the well: Ruckus counting imaginary piles of coins while his face reflected the most horrid greed anyone had ever seen. It was enough to scare that burgher into honesty.

Should the mayor or any of the town council visit the well while puffed up with the pride of office and responsibility, Ruckus mirrored them in such a way that it seemed as if pins had been stuck in overblown balloons, and they went away thoroughly deflated.

The country bumpkin who had spoiled the hay by sleeping through the rain saw Ruckus assume a shape that seemed to be a loathesome, old slug stuck to the side of the well. Certain it was that he would be lively at his chores for weeks to come. Indeed, no one left the well without cause for reflection. Consequently, it could be said without exaggeration, that the people of Once Was were good.

By recognizing in Ruckus their worst qualities, they were made to think about them, and to do something about them. Gradually and gradually, over many generations the people of Once Was became better and better. Whatever a man's own faults, there was always consideration for his neighbor, and kindness hung in the air like the smell of spring lilacs. Indeed, compared to townspeople around the rest of the world, the Once-Wasians were Saints!

Then a sad change came. The Genie of Progress eventually visited this little town, as it had so many idyllic places on the globe. Naturally it brought with it electricity and plumbing. Once Was officially became Now Town.

Before long, children were being born who had never visited the well. This did nothing for their dispositions. Many of the old folks continued to visit the well, if not to quaff a cup of well water, then at least to steal an over-the-shoulder glance at Ruckus. More and more, however, these "old ways" were suspect, officially discouraged as not in keeping with Now Town's new image.

As the well was used less and less, the water became more turbid and fetid. The clarity went out of it, and soon a skulking old man could not be sure anymore if he were making out the dim shape of Ruckus, or an old toad that had hopped into the well. After a new generation had grown up, the bottom of the well could not be seen at all. There was no doubt in the minds of the old folk that Ruckus was still there, for the waters would bubble and froth with unseen activity. Some even said that at the bottom of the well Ruckus was in a fury.

That talk was part of the "old ways," so it was officially decided to board up the well. There was a general fear of someone's falling in. After many years, no one was alive who had ever seen Ruckus.

A subtle change came over the town.

If the butcher were weighing some meat, his thumb was certain to be on the scale. The Fixit-Shop began using inferior parts, but the prices were higher than before. Now all the little boys raided the jampots so that jam ceased to be anything special at all. The moneylenders doubled their rates and gave out insolence in the bargain. Workers everywhere fell asleep at any hour of the day. Soon the town was a moral ruin.

Well, what of Ruckus during all this? You may be surprised to learn that he had not stayed at the bottom of the well. No indeed! Each night, when everyone was fast asleep, he was out making mischief. He would worry the cows in the barn all night long so that in the morning their milk was sour as old beer. He would pull the pins from cart wheels, or saw a roof beam nearly through. In the morning the cart would lose a wheel on the way to market, and the roof tumble in, so that carpenters and wheelers were cursed from one end of Now town to another.

The next night, Ruckus would be at work again. He did not stop at mischief and pranks, but often would climb inside some sleeping head and work his mischief there. The next day that man or woman would behave in very uncharacteristic ways. He might begin the day by beating the dog, thrashing his children, and bickering with his wife. By nightfall, all who had crossed his path had come to rue that day. Such a man was said to be "kicking up a ruckus," although by now so many years had passed that no one—not even the oldest graybeards—could recall the little old man at the bottom of the well. Moss of bright green and dark yellow grew over the weathered, old wood that covered it. From time to time, a rotted chunk would drop off and fall away. But there was no longer any fear of falling into the well. So many years had passed that no one even remembered the curious mound of rocks, mortar, and decaying boards at the very center of the town square, and for what it had been used. No, there was no fear of falling into it. The well and its denizen had become a "nothing but."

The father would tell his son, "That's nothing but an old platform used for making speeches many years ago." The mother would tell her daughter gaily, "Years ago, there was a merry-go-round there. All that remains is the old hub."

The children, however, as children are wont to do, told more truth about the well than any of their learned elders. "A ghost lives there," Tom would tell little Janie to frighten her. "No," said Janie, "it's the hole of a big snake that comes out at night to bite you!"

"A troll lives there that eats people," said Billy, the grocer's boy.

"Naah," said Arnold, the churchwarden's own gem, "a giant black bat flies out at night to suck blood from everyone in town."

Hobgoblins are never forgotten by children, so in their own wise way, they knew what was at the bottom of the well.

The truth is Now Town had become as bad as any other town. The first jail was built, and crime had now left the home for the streets as well. When such crises develop, it does not take long for many to come forth with The Answers.

"All our problems are directly attributable to the farmers," intoned Now Town's most prosperous banker.

"The money lenders have squeezed us dry and pirated our land," raged a red-faced man, waving his fist like a bludgeon.

"Blondes, blondes are to blame," cried a swarthy man.

"You don't have to look beyond the unions for the source of our troubles," said the town's largest employer.

"Down with the Establishment!" shouted the Anti-establishment. "Down with the fascist insect that preys on the people!"

"Down with the Anti-establishment," rejoined their numbers. "Down with the parasites who feed on the social body but won't work!"

"Down! Down!" yelled the pro-anti-establishment.

"Down with everybody!" hollered the anti-pro-anti-establishment.

"Why not?!" added the nihilists.

"Spiralling prices are concomitant to economic suicide, and for this only the Public is to be blamed," said the Government.

"Retailers!" said a Middleman.

"Wholesalers!" said Another.

As usual, the clergy had the final say. "Good, old-fashioned sin," said the Bishop, rubbing his hands together gleefully.

It was not long before everyone saw all of his own bad traits in someone else!

It was about this time that a little girl noticed that the shadows all had gone away. She liked to play games with her shadow, but it seemed that each day the shadow became paler and paler until it had faded away. She thought it would come back when next the sun shone brightly, but alas her playmate had fled forever.

While with her mother in the town square at noon she noticed that no one cast a shadow anymore. Where had they all gone? Yet the trees and mountains still cast shadows as if nature retained a secret balance man could not maintain.

II.

It was about this time that a young boy was born who would become the salvation. He was not a comely lad; indeed, as he grew older a great bump began to grow upon him as if he had taken all the sins of the world upon his back. For this ugliness his fellow students beat him religiously, and a day never passed that he did not return from school swollen from blows. He never complained, to the despair of his parents who despaired of his good nature.

"Why grieve for my life?" he would say in his great wisdom. "If I did not think such a life would suit me, why then did I choose it?"

"Your life comes from God," they replied, "and cannot be your own choosing."

"But our teachings tell us God is just. If I had no choice in my life, then God cannot be just. Surely, therefore, I chose my life and body to show that God can be glorified in the face of the greatest adversity."

But his parents could not be consoled. "You could have been a doctor; you could have been a lawyer; and you had to do this to yourself!" And they turned away and were disgraced by him.

In time he came to find his life in the spiritual communion of sky and mountain, animal and forest, and he was at peace as a shepherd.

One day he came to a place where an old, gnarled oak grew, bent and mishapen like his own body, yet stately and wise in its life. Looking up, he saw a crook in a limb that held a large hollow—just the size of his hump. Clawing his way up, for he was none too agile with his hump, he found he could rest with his hump in the hollow and still watch the sheep from his high vantage.

He hadn't been there very long when who should come along but the little girl who had lost her shadow playmate.

"Are you lost, little girl?" called the shepherd boy from his tree.

"No," said the girl, "but my shadow is, and I have come to find it."

"How can you lose your shadow?" asked the boy.

"I'm sure I don't know," said the girl, "but no one in *this* town has a shadow anymore, and what's more, nobody cares. Except I do, because mine was the best playmate of all. It was always thinking up new games for us. Why, I got some of my best ideas from it. Now I feel like only *half* a person."

"Well, you can't stay down there. Darkness is coming on and you shall soon be as lost as your shadow. Climb up into my tree and you shall be safe for the night."

Wasting no time, the little girl scrambled up like a monkey. So many games with her shadow had made her quite a tomboy. Soon she was snug against the shepherd; for by some strange quirk his limb held another hollow that matched exactly the shape of the little girl.

Before very long, the sun began to weary of the world, yawned, and putting on his evening cap and lighting a bedtime candle, set into the dark world below.

Just then the shepherd boy noticed something very curious. From an odd little mound under his limb, away down on the ground, darkness was scurrying like so many furtive rats. The little girl saw where he was looking, and watched too.

"That is the old well," she said. "My grandmother used to tell me about it. The center of town was once here, many years ago."

As they watched, the blackness grew thicker. It was like seeing ink spill slowly from an inkwell in all directions.

"What can it be?" said the boy, for in all of his young wisdom he had never seen anything like that.

"Perhaps it is the shadows—all the shadows fanning out with the night."

"Can they live in the well by day?" said the boy, shaking his head in disbelief as the shadows lengthened from the well.

"Maybe mine is among them," cried the girl clapping her hands in glee.

That night they hardly slept at all, so afraid were they of missing the dawn. Sure enough, just as the sun took off his sleeping cap, blew out his evening candle, and called the moon to bed, the shadows began to creep along the ground towards the well. The boy and the girl watched, their faces, round with wonder, shining from the tree like sun and moon cheek to cheek in the sky. And as they watched, the shadows came. As battalions of night retreating from day they came, here and there at the rear a straggler like a reluctant alley-cat dragged in by day before he has had his fill of night.

In a moment, all shadows disappeared down the well, not even a blade of grass bending to that phantom army's passing. The boy and the girl looked at each other, uncertain of what they had seen; then taking her hand, he helped her down from the tree, for in their long night's vigil he had promised to help her find her shadow.

Where the shadows had entered the well, there were rickety boards laid over the well top. Pulling these away, the boy could see—oh, so far below—the faint glimmer of water. They dropped a stone and it plummeted for eternity before a hollow splash echoed back to them.

Without fear they began to climb down the sides of the well, without fear because the power of the well was now theirs, and the promise below sustained them. The sides were not slippery since it had been so long that water had risen in the well, and the stones of the side made sure holds for their small hands and feet.

For all of the morning they descended, and at noon, just as the sun peered over the rim of the well, as if seeking a draught at the meridian of his parched progress, they touched bottom.

They stood on a stone where the sides of the well bottomed out, yet beneath them the water spread in every direction below. Now they were not so sure of themselves, but the little girl climbed up on his hump and the boy dove down into the waters. The deeper he dove, the clearer the waters became, and soon he came to a little town under the waters that looked both like Now Town now and Once Was once.

Now they could see that they had just swum up a well exactly like the one they had climbed down. It was as if everything was a shadow reflection of everything they had left above.

"What a curious world in which down is up," said the shepherd.

"And left is right," chimed in one of the shadows.

"And black is white," said another; for shadows were crowding all around them, anxious to meet the newcomers.

"Good may be evil, and evil may be good," rasped an old man who dragged himself towards them, his trunk like an ancient oak, his legs like roots pulled after him.

"Welcome to the Land of Shadows," he said. "I am Ruckus, the Ancient of Night."

The children began to speak, but he held up his hand. "We know you both already. Your world is familiar to us, but our world is no longer known to your people. You are the first to visit here by day, although you come every night."

The boy and the girl protested that they had never been there before, but Ruckus only smiled and said, "There is so little time, and so many secrets to impart."

Then the children fell silent, and the shadows gathered around as Ruckus told:

THE SAGA OF THE SHADOWS.

"Once upon a time, your world and our world were in the same place at the same time, but some of us wanted to live in the light and gradually the two worlds moved apart, though they never became separate because separation does not really exist. The well was always open then, and the waters that flowed between kept vital the flow of life. The well was our link with you and your link with us, but in time some of you didn't like what you saw in the well, didn't want to be reminded of from whence you had come, and felt you didn't need the darkness anymore. And so you shut up the well, shut up your shadows inside, and tried to close us off from the light. But we need the light as much as you need your shadows—the living water flows *both* ways.

The great secret is that you are our shadows, just as we are your shadows. Our world is not another world apart from yours; your world is our shadow world and we are yours. Your vitality comes from the well to your world, and ours comes from that same world that hurts our eyes. You do not see very well in the dark; we do not see very well by day, but together our eyes have true vision.

But your eyes have lost their shadow awareness, and without the well your world is drying up. Things are too one-sided for your world now. You can know only the sun, and have forgotten the moon.

You no longer recognize, acknowledge us, and this makes us nasty. Our sleep is plagued by nightmares from your world, and it is only in your sleep that we can remind you of us by disturbing your dreams, as our dreams are troubled by you. We can do nothing by ourselves. Your world must want the vital water to flow again as much as we do. Shadows belong at home where they can be managed, not running around in the world making mischief."

Wearily he finished, and his last words were like the sighing of the wind through an ancient gnarled oak. The little girl had found her shadow now, and the two held hands and sat quietly listening.

The shepherd boy knew it was time for leave-taking, and the little girl and her shadow rose to go. A certain sadness overcame the boy, and he turned back to question Ruckus.

"Tell me," he said, "who is my shadow?"

"You will know that only yourself, but I can tell you," said Ruckus, with a twinkling of ancient eyes, "that an old man's shadow is a young boy."

Just then the young girl leaped upon the boy's back for the long swim up to the light, but where she had held to his hump before, now she slipped from his back, for the hump was gone. He had been a little old man and now was young. Before him, Ruckus bent like an ancient oak in a gale of ancient wind.

As they swam up, her arms around his neck now, they heard from below, Ruckus' voice calling, "Tell them about us!"

Primer for "Ruckus in the Well"

It may appear to the reader that this story was given its creative impetus by the quote from Jung which prefaces this tale. However, the story was written in the year 1970 completely by the active imagination process, having begun itself in a dream which the dreamer/author completed upon awakening. Late in 1982, while commencing the primer on the shadow, I ran across Jung's line in *The Archetypes and the Collective Unconscious*. The lines following also merit quoting:

> True, whoever looks into the mirror of the water will see first of all his own face. Whoever goes to himself risks a confrontation with himself. The mirror does not flatter, it faithfully shows whatever looks into it; namely, the face we never show to the world because we cover it with the *persona*, the mask of the actor. But the mirror lies behind the mask and shows the true face.
>
> This confrontation is the first test of courage on the inner way, a test sufficient to frighten off most people, for the meeting with ourselves belongs to the more unpleasant things that can be avoided so long as we can project everything negative into the environment. But if we are able to see our own shadow and can bear knowing about it, then a small part of the problem has already been solved: we have at least brought up the personal unconscious. The shadow is a living part of the personality and therefore wants to live with it in some form.

And, finally, in the next paragraph Jung writes: "The shadow is a tight passage, a narrow door, whose painful constriction no one is spared who goes down to the deep well." (*The Archetypes and the Collective Unconscious*, p. 21) Thus, in the symbology of "the mirror of the water" and "the deep well," the archetype of the shadow in my personal unconscious expressed itself in dream and active imagination in creating this story.

As our story begins, everything is in perfect harmony because the waters of the unconscious (the well) are utilized daily by the inhabitants who acknowledge the little old man known as Ruckus. This daily acknowledgment of "the ugliest man who had ever been" is a healthy process whereby each person can recognize his own worst traits and thereby correct them, or at least, not *project* them onto others, which may be the source of most contention in our world, individually and internationally.

In "Ruckus in the Well" we see how negative qualities of the shadow may be projected onto others. The most important thing to remember is that the more rapport we have with the unconscious mind, the more we strive to acknowledge the archetypes of our personal unconscious, and the more we bring them into consciousness, the less trouble we have in dealing with others and the more harmony we have in our personal lives.

Looking into the waters of the well, therefore, symbolizes looking into the unconscious. The other side of the mask of the persona faces not outwardly towards society and those we seek to charm, but inwardly towards the mirror/waters of the unconscious. Indeed, the tendency in the direction of the unconscious suggests the process of *repression,* whereby elements unpleasing to the ego are pushed down into the unconscious so that they need not be faced. Akin to an electro-magnetic field, *libido* is a term denoting the psychic energy generated by the psyche. Libido is the energy carrying the archetypes on their projected journey out of the unconscious where they become our personal *projections,* as we shall see in "The Crystal People."

The shadow lurks behind the persona. The ego beholds itself in the shining splendor of the persona, but if the ego turns inwardly to the mirror of the unconscious, it sees its dark brother, the shadow, encompassing all the undesirable aspects which the ego cannot face and which are repressed, therefore, into the unconscious. Unfortunately, the more our nasty qualities are repressed instead of being examined in the devastating light of consciousness, the more we project these qualities onto others. Naturally, the more we project, the more we encounter nasty people all around us, little realizing that in a sense they are our own creations.

A simple test for revealing the repressed characteristics of one's own shadow is as follows: Describe someone (of the same sex) you know personally, preferably someone with whom you have worked or lived on a daily basis. Now why is it that the person irritates you so? Precisely what are the characteristics you find so distressing? When you have finished charting *that* person's undesirable qualities, you have in effect described your own shadow, naked at last in the light of the projection's unveiling.

However, once we have at least partial awareness of our faults, we can catch ourselves in the process of projecting these faults onto others; hence, our relations with others will begin to improve as we learn to place the blame where it is due—at home with ourselve and not *out there* with others. At the same time, the awareness of our undesirable characteristics can motivate us to do something about them; therefore, we can change for the better.

In our story of the shadow figure Ruckus, the rapport of the townspeople with the well symbolizes the ego's attention to the waters of the unconscious. On a daily basis, each one in the town is instructed as to his or her shortcomings. There is a constant renewal and refreshening of consciousness by the waters of the unconscious; hence, the well is crystal clear because "the deep spring" pours in "new waters each day."

Archetypes are primordial images, so Ruckus is very ancient, having been at the bottom of the well longer than anyone can remember. But the ego, collective and individual, of the town of Once Was, loses its rapport and harmony with the unconscious, and the waters become so "turbid and fetid" that the perception of the shadowy Ruckus is lost. Finally, the complete repression of the shadow is symbolized by the boarding up of the well, and all contact with the "old ways" is lost forever.

The shadow is then projected; Ruckus comes out of the well "making mischief." The term *shadow possession* is used to describe the overwhelming of the ego by the undesirable elements of the shadow. In such a case, the persona is also overwhelmed, and the ego ceases to exercise its usual autonomy. Such a man is said to be "kicking up a ruckus." Indeed, the shadowy Ruckus has climbed inside his sleeping head to "work his mischief there." Thus in possession, consciousness unknowingly relinquishes autonomy. The individual becomes the victim of emotional *affects*. As Jung tells us:

> To become conscious of it [the shadow] involves recognizing the dark aspects of the personality as present and real. This act is the essential condition for any kind of self-knowledge, and it therefore, as a rule, meets with considerable resistance. . . . Closer examination of the dark characteristics—that is, the inferiorities constituting the shadow—reveals that they have an *emotional* nature, a kind of *autonomy*, and accordingly an *obsessive* or, better, *possessive* quality. Emotion, incidentally, is not an activity of the individual but something that happens to him. Affects occur usually where adaptation is weakest, and at the same time they reveal the reason for its weakness, namely a certain degree of inferiority and the existence of a lower level of personality. On this lower level with its uncontrolled or scarcely controlled emotions one behaves more or less like a primitive, who is not only the passive victim of his affects but also singularly incapable of moral judgment. (*Aion*)

The latter words, "singularly incapable of moral judgment," may be used to describe the German nation under Adolph Hitler in the Second World War. As Hitler spoke to the mobs, he had an uncanny ability to draw on his own shadow, so that he ranted and raved like a man possessed and the crowds echoed his individual possession with their own collective possession. When the shadow is at large, scapegoats must be found. Discussing the Nazi party, Jung said, it "destroyed man's moral autonomy and set up the nonsensical totalitarianism of the State." (vol. 9, i, p. 252)

A rather humorous projection of the collective German shadow focused on Sir Winston Churchill, the British prime minister. He was shown on Nazi propaganda posters brandishing a tommy-gun, while beneath his picture were Hitler's words: "For over five years this man has been chasing around Europe like a madman in search of something he could set on fire. Unfortunately he again and again finds hirelings who open the gates of their country to this international incendiary." The words best describe Hitler's own inflammatory tendencies; yet the projections of both love *and* hate are blind indeed. And, as our story tells us, "It was not long before everyone saw all of his own bad traits in someone else!"

"It was about this time that a little girl noticed that the shadows all had gone away." She and the humpbacked shepherd boy descend into the unconscious (the well) in search of the shadows, which they have seen returning to the well at daybreak. The shadows are now out at night only, disturbing the human dreams. The daylight world, which symbolizes the conscious mind, has repressed the shadows and the unconscious world by boarding up the well and shutting out the shadows. But psychic harmony is based upon the dynamic flow of energy between conscious and unconscious. As Ruckus tells them in The Saga of the Shadows, "Things are too one-sided for your world now. You can only know the sun, and have forgotten the moon.

"You no longer recognize, acknowledge us, and this makes us nasty. Our sleep is plagued by nightmares from your world, and it is only in your sleep that we can remind you of us by disturbing your dreams, as our dreams are troubled by you. We can do nothing by ourselves. Your world must want the vital water to flow again as much as we do. Shadows belong at home where they can be managed, not running around in the world making mischief."

Ruckus' last words to the boy and girl, as they prepare for "the long swim up to the light," are "Tell them about us!" This is the main characteristic of all the archetypes of the unconscious—they seek relatedness to consciousness. The more repressed they are, the more nasty they become.

But beyond making us aware of our worse side, the shadow has a more profound meaning. The young boy who would "become the salvation" for the townspeople by bringing to them the message from below, which we may assume shall restore the psychic balance, takes on the hero's role. He possesses a spiritual quality beyond his years, usually associated with the archetype of *the wise old man*. Like the ego, the boy draws strength from his descent into the unconscious. And before the ego can be its own master, it must assimilate the shadow.

In *The Phenomenology of the Spirit in Fairytales* (*The Archetypes and the Collective Unconscious*, vol. 9, i) Jung tells us that the spirit, symbolic of spiritual meaning, like the wise old man, can take the form of a boy or youth, signifying the higher personality of the psyche, the *self*. In effect, the shadow is the self's opposite number; therefore Jung notes that the youth and the "Graybeard" belong together. This, I suppose, is the answer to the boy's query to Ruckus: "Who is my shadow?"

"You will know that only for yourself, but I can tell you," said Ruckus, with a twinkling of ancient eyes, "that an old man's shadow is a young boy." Thus the symbol of the boy points beyond in meaning to what Jung called the *child* archetype, which through associated ideas of regeneration and rebirth, anticipate the immortality of the soul.

> In this idea the all-embracing nature of psychic wholeness is expressed. Wholeness is never comprised within the compass of the conscious mind—it includes the indefinite and indefinable extent of the unconscious as well. Wholeness, empirically speaking, is therefore of immeasurable extent, older and younger than consciousness and enfolding it in time and space. (CW, vol. 9, i, p. 178)

The journey of individuation, the pathway to wholeness, involves making a friend of the shadow, which appears at first in the role of antagonist, because this archetype represents a despised component of consciousness, some aspect of the conscious ego which has proved unacceptable to consciousness, and therefore repressed into the unconscious. Hence, Ruckus appears initially as "the ugliest man who had ever been."

The shadow may appear in many other guises in dreams or fairytales. Wolves, serpents, lions, whales represent the ego's fear of being devoured by the unconscious, since the ego was once contained within the unconscious, and begins to emerge from the unconscious as it leaves the infantile stage and approaches adolescence. At the same time, the wild and primitive quality of the shadow figure suggests its instinctive, unadaptable nature. Therefore, it must be tamed and civilized.

Most terrifying of all is the shadow's appearance in dreams as a monster. Here I would like to share with the reader a Big Dream of my own. For many days I had been reading fairytales for examples of the archetypes in preparation for a seminar I was teaching entitled "Pathways of Individuation." Consciously I noted that whenever a monster or figure of menace was encountered in a story, if the protagonist responded with love and kindness, then the figure magically changed into something innocuous or into a prince or princess; thus one's *response* was the key to the shadow's challenge. That night I fell asleep and encountered in the dream a terrifying monster, but I remembered what I had learned consciously, and began reciting like a mantra to the monster, "I love you, I love you, I love you," over and over again, for I knew my rejection of the shadow had made it appear so monstrous. Then, sure enough, the figure changed into a quite ordinary human being.

Because the shadow may become a positive help in life, and since it is far better to have a friend rather than an enemy on that difficult journey to individual wholeness, integration of the archetype is the result of recognition of the shadow. Finally, the shadow demonstrates a valuable lesson of the correspondence of inner and outer worlds; that is, what we put out in the way of vibrations is what we get back. Hate returns hate, and love returns love.

THE MASK THAT WORE THE MAN

Once upon a time there was a boy born foolish enough to be an orphan. Since he had no family to care for him, he was shunted from foster home to asylum, and then back again, never remaining more than a month at either. Because he was truly foolish, and without a name at birth, he became known as "the fool," or sometimes, "the *poor* fool."

Besides not having a name of his own, he also did not have a face—to speak of—for the moment he was out the door none of his custodians or foster parents could remember what he looked like. If pressed for a description, they would throw up their hands and say "nondescript!" And, indeed, no adjective ever fitted the boy better.

The essence of his foolishness lay in his self-effacement. Just as he never could be remembered, he could be counted on never to have an impact on anyone whomsoever. Further, no one remembered anything he said, if, indeed, he ever said anything. Forgotten even when he was present, it was not long before society cast him out utterly. He would have been a beggar if anyone had given him anything, but since no one did, he lived like a wild animal and took his food from the trees and the forest floor. But he fared as badly in the company of trees, animals, and insects as he had in the company of man. Trees would lie in ambush to whip him with their branches, and racing before the wind like a hell-bent wheel, a tumblebush would go out of its way to stab him with a thorn or sting him with a nettle. "Take that! Whoever you are!"

Bees would assemble in attack formation when he was still miles from their nest. Some days he might spend the entire time lying in a mudbank to draw out the thousand stings left in him by the yellow-jacketed hordes.

Dogs sought him out even beyond the bounds of their own territory. When he was still miles from a village, one old avenger, sensing him, commenced a din that alerted all the dogs in the country. Often it seemed that his body bore the marks of their every fang.

When he was in the middle of nowhere and no barking could be heard, no trees, bees, or bushes nearby, from heaven itself there might fall a reminder, noxious and slimy, that the birds had not forgotten him.

Although cast out by human society, people welcomed his occasional appearances as opportunities for venting their most ingenious cruelties. Since he was important to no one but himself, no one defended him or resented the violences done to him. The law protected him not at all, for if ever anyone was an outlaw it was surely he. No minority, however inconsequential, could possibly identify with him. To do so would be to deprive themselves of their own identity. How this poor fool survived was a miracle only God knew.

One day he chanced to hear in the distance a great noise of music, dancing, and laughter. Although usually giving a wide berth to crowds, the din was such that he thought he could steal upon them and observe from a discreet distance. What he came upon was the travelling wagon of a troupe of itinerant actors, camped at the edge of a country fair, preparing to perform a play. One side of the wagon was down to make a stage. Wandering hither and thither around the stage the actors seemed utterly without purpose, aimless in all their movements. None the less, the poor fool continued to watch. Their conversation seemed of no import, their faces were as plain and innocuous as his own, observed the poor fool.

As the time of the performance neared, the actors' movements increased, they scurried about like ants whose purpose is known only in the secret of the hill. Here one drew on a crimson robe of royal hue; there another bound himself in armor of militant sheen. And when the curtain went up and the masks had been put on, the transformation was complete. These ordinary men and women were now kings and queens, knights and ladies, gods and devils!

The change in individual personality was amazing. Hands of the actors, which had hung so woodenly at their sides, now came alive, sweeping the air, invoking visions of castles, vast plains resounding to the clash of armies, and the words of the actors' speech soared like a flock of birds, darting thither and yon, cartwheeling in the air, performing acrobatics of phrase and nuance. The reaction of the crowd was as the fool's: this was magical, a panorama of ecstasy beyond the dullness of day-to-day life.

Many hours after the theatrical wagon had shuttered for the night, the fool still sat huddled in his hiding place, his brain teeming with the sights and words he had seen and heard. All the dogs were deep in doggy dreams, and the moon had set in a far corner of the forest to sleep away what was left of the night, when the fool stole out from his hiding place. Returning to the cave where he lived, the poor fool pondered what he had seen . . . long, long . . . . And then he knew.

"They are nobodies themselves," he thought of the actors. "Poor fools just like me. But the costumes—The masks!—make them Everyman."

The fool now knew a truth many men never learned, a secret of the ways of the world, and knowing a truth, he was no longer a fool.

He resolved then to create a mask for himself. Tears smarted his eyes as he set to work. Never had he a mask of his own! All those years of being set upon by boys, bees, brambles, beagles, and blackbirds! And now, the beautiful simplicity of the truth that had eluded him. Well, he would fashion a mask that would be The Face of Everyman. Yes, Everyman, but Everyman in such a way that He had never seen Himself before.

By the candlelight he labored in his cave, day and night. His face, sallow and empty heretofore, now resembled a candle itself, glowing and ruddy with the light of the truth that possessed him. Hardly stopping to eat or rest, he worked on and on, a chip removed here, something added there, all the while rehearsing his gestures and speech before a mirror on the wall. And, then, long years later, he was ready for the world. He emerged from his cave and set forth.

The fool had transformed himself into a juggler—no!—The Magician!

When this *new* person entered his first town, dogs bowed their heads respectfully or heeled behind him, as if recognizing their master. The parliament of birds in the town square ceased their haggling and waited intently for his speech. Flowers bloomed all at once and spread their petals at his feet. A crowd gathered, each person speculating in hushed tones about the identity of this magnificent stranger.

And then he began! Commencing a conversation with the one person nearest him, the crowd closing about, without missing a word, he engaged a second person, a third, and fourth in conversation. In no time he was juggling a dozen conversations in the air until it seemed like skipping rope when many are already jumping and others enter to be added to the game; then another, another, and yet another until it seems the sky cannot hold so many in the air at once.

With his magical mask each saw in his face a reflection of the face each kept hidden within his innermost heart, the Face of Everyman. Even the most surly and reticent were moved to call to him a friendly greeting, although they never gave the time of day to their own townsmen. Upon being greeted, The Magician might toss a pun lightly into the air, to juggle it with a dozen variations, then, grabbing that person's reply, he might transform it with a wave of his hand into a multi-metaphored bird of outrageous plumage.

Puns, of course, were the children's favorites. They began shrieking with delight when he was still on the outskirts of their village.

For the housewives he had flights of fancy such as they had heard only once before—on their wedding nights—and never since. Castles of romance he tiered into the air, with silver waterfalls of assonance, and towers topped by purple hyperbole. His face for them was Prince Charming's, the long forsaken one of their dreams come at last!

From the itinerant peddlar to the most established shopkeepers, he had one specialty that kept them in stitches. It was "The Insult." Years of fawning before the fickle needs of an unappreciative public had made each bourgeois just *wish* that he had said *this* or *that* to so-and-so's abuse. Now he gave them what they wanted with years of scorn compounded as interest. This act began with a swift rejoinder, added innuendo, progressing to aspersions about birthright, and finally, when it must be assumed that the imaginary antagonist was beside himself with rage, concluded with dismissal and cold disdain.

For a cleric, The Magician's voice became the voice of God, juggling Old and New Testaments, speaking out of a cloud, or a burning bush, or from His mighty judgment throne. Somber as a serpent, his tongue flicking flame, The Magician spoke to the ungodly as one long oppressed whose hour now had come round, and the pious would cringe before him who could transform their wine into burning blood.

Ah, for the children his true wit was saved, for children know that foolishness is wisdom turned inside out, so that grownups cannot recognize it, and he played with each child like the Imaginary Playmate come true, whispering confidences that only the innermost heart could share.

His fame went before him wherever he went, and the old world which had sought to trip him up at every turn now had become his stepping stone.

II.
THE MASK THAT WORE THE MAN

Long he had forsaken his cave and taken permanent residence at the Ritz, that is, when he was not being wined and dined at the palaces of royalty. One night, in a distant empire, at a state dinner in his honor he was given brandy made from the particularly potent petals of a Polynesian flower. Coming back to his suite, he fell into a deep and oppressive sleep, omitting to remove his mask, something he had forgotten never before. His first impression was of stifling to death, and, indeed, his breathing became labored and agitated while he slept on. Then he dreamed that he was back in the old days, when he was shunned by society and did not have his protective mask. In the dream, nature was again venting its displeasure upon him, but what made the dream so horrible was that every creature wore a Punch-like mask, and all the masks were the same!

Dogs nipped at his calves and ankles, their canine teeth slashing from under the masks' wooden molars. Bees attacked, again gigantic in size, and their stings were borne in the tip of their outlandishly large Punch noses. The tumblebushes were all around again, wheeling to and fro and knocking him off his feet, only this time they had Punch-like heads, with eyes that rolled up and down with the rolling of their bodies. Crows were flailing him with their leathery wings, and each also bore Punch's face. From the crows came a cacophony of commentary, which the victim recognized as the table conversation from the very dinner he had attended that night. This nightmare assault assailed him for some time that night, until finally he slept the sleep of sweet oblivion.

He was awakened by reporters come to interview him,

leaped up from the bed at the doorbell's ring, and began at once to give a sparkling interview, for he had slept in his clothes as well. The interview over, a famous actress came to collect him for lunch, over which they lingered until time for his matinee performance at which he made all the drama critics his artistic slaves. Another state dinner followed, and here he agreed to a high political position. Several weeks passed in this manner without his realizing that he still wore the mask.

When he discovered this, he was startled, and, indeed, could not remember when he had last been without it. Peering into a mirror, he sought his own eyes through the slits in the mask, but a flinty contempt stared back at him.

Well, this has gone far enough, he thought. I shall rest from the world for a while; maybe even visit my old cave where I fashioned this chap. While thinking thusly, he began to tug at the mask's edges to loosen its grip and remove it from his face. In amazement, he found he could not get it off! Around his head and throat, the skin had crystallized to a hardness like the mask, so that where he left off and the mask began could no longer be determined. Then, to his horror, a deep rumbling began to form in his throat, laughter not his, but someone else's, someone who laughed no longer for him but at him. Then he knew that for the rest of the days and nights of his life, the mask would wear the man.

Primer for "The Mask That Wore the Man"

"We sell ourselves by the way we appear." I shall return to these words again because they have a dual meaning, and that is why "The Face of Everyman" is in two parts. Our eventual defense and buffer zone against the world's cruelties is the *persona,* a mask that hides out intimate inner self, protecting us from hurt. The first day of school is a potential trauma because we are in a sense psychically naked. The ego of the growing child soon learns that the impression one makes on others enables one to get what he or she wants. Gradually, therefore, through a system of trial and error, we learn to put on the kind of face that will please Mommy and Daddy, siblings, and teachers. And with that face in place, we find our desires satisfied once more—not as completely as in the womb, but enough to make life worthwhile.

As children grow older and begin to mix more and more with the world beyond their own family, they find that the way they are received by their schoolmates is based upon how they appear to other persons. Thus the children begin to create a mask, or *persona,* in order to sell themselves to others, and also to protect the vulnerable inner person so subject to hurt and rejection. In the privacy of our own room, where we can be what we really want to be and not what we have to be to suit others, we may throw our mask under the bed and pig out or overdose on what satisfies us solely.

The mask is usually in place at the end of adolescence, but sometimes not, accounting in part for the large number of teen-age suicides. When we feel that no one understands us at all, particularly our parents and peers at school, then life may seem too painful to go on. In later years, if we look once more through our high school and college yearbooks, we find that the Biggest Persons On Campus were those who made the best impressions; hence it was the *persona* that got them what they wanted. The *persona* is a refinement of social adaptation. When one has not made this adaptation, he receives a lukewarm or hostile reception from society. Such is the case of the "poor fool" in our story. However, by observing actors he is able to successfully create a face to which Everyman will respond favorably. So armed he reverses his fortunes.

Besides protecting us, the *persona* also serves us as our personality, the social adaptation that we as individuals must make to society as a whole. Generally dreams of wearing apparel are symbolic of the *persona.* One woman I knew had a recurring dream about standing in front of her closet unable to make up her mind as to which dress to wear, all the time knowing she would be late to work if she did not make up her mind soon. In reality, she was not at ease in public and had trouble speaking in groups. The dream reflects her persona problem. The *persona* is like a role in a play. We create our first persona to please our parents and peers; this suits us until about the ages 27–30 whereupon we modify our mask to suit ourselves. This persona seems to fit until about the age of 56–58, when we find once more that we seem to have outgrown the old mask.

When we play at being someone else, that is all right if we do not forget the real self within. If we do, we have sold ourselves in a way that betrays our highest purpose and responsibility. We have sold out to acceptability. In time actors often come to identify with the roles they play most frequently, or with the mask or image they have in the eyes of society. Then the *persona* or mask no longer serves them, but they serve the mask.

As in our story, "The Mask That Wore the Man," there is a psychic danger, a potential trap for the ego consciousness because the *persona* is created to serve the ego. If the *persona* is especially successful in its effect upon the world, then the ego may so identify with it that it winds up serving the *persona,* master become slave.

Thus one walks a razor's edge between pleasing others and being true to one's self, which is at the center of the psyche and thus is our spiritual center in life. Whereas the *persona* can betray us, the self never can, being our impetus towards higher development, transformation, and new birth.

There is a film, "E.T." (for extra-terrestrial) which we can analyze as analogous to the *persona.* E.T. (the entity) has been described as resembling a turtle without its shell. Since our *persona* is molded and based on the conduct of our society, it is suitable only to that specific society. It may be inappropriate for another culture even on our own planet. But if we journeyed to another planet we could almost be certain that our *personae* would be utterly worthless. Indeed, to the denizens of another planet, it would seem as if we had none, were in effect naked.

So E.T., the turtle without his shell, cannot relate to the socially-adapted adults of our world; yet he relates beautifully to the children. The film's universal appeal can be attributed to our identification of E.T. with the child within us, the open, honest, foresaken, and nearly forgotten child we were before we had to put on the *persona's* hard shell to protect our ultimate vulnerability. The children understand E.T. and understand the danger that he faces if the adults capture him. In this sense, he is a metaphor of what children must sacrifice by growing up, putting on the mask that pleases others. Although the *persona* is necessary in protecting us from being too vulnerable, there is a certain sadness attached to leaving this state of openness and innocence; and, as the story shows, a certain danger attached if we come to identify too closely with the new personalities we assume.

Peg Kranz ©

THE SEED'S SECRET

When The Wanderer had passed this way once again, He strew some seeds over the world to make the world green and to give Him much joy. But He moved quickly on His way through the universe, and left within each only the small seed of His Own Light.

It was winter on the earth when He passed our way, and Mother Nature was cold and unreceptive to the seeds. Her body was awaiting the great surge of spring, when she stirred in her sleep, shook her loins, and the great cycle of life began again within her.

The seeds lay in a great horde over her body, and on the first day the rain rained all day. "Now," said the seeds, "we're soaked through and through. Just right for our beginning."

On the next day, a cold wind blew out of the north, and some of the seeds began to complain.

"We were told that accommodations might not be the best, but this is absurd." Some of them even began to wish that they had never been strewn.

The third day was no easier. The ground was hardened by the wind, and not a root could be put down.

The rest of the week the rains came back, softening the earth, but driving the seeds deeper and deeper into the ground. Some of them were borne away on rivulets of water, others bounced from place to place as giant raindrops struck them.

"Ouch," and "Oouch!" said the seeds as the rain hammered their heads. "If only the sun would come out!" chorused all of them.

"What a beautiful seedling I could be," said another, "if only I had the right warm soil around me, and just enough sun to start me sprouting."

"Oh," said its neighbor, "I don't ask much. Just a little sun through the clouds and I can manage as well as any."

But the rains carried on through all of that month and the next. This was impossible to the seeds. Anyone listening who could talk seed talk would have heard a whole field full of complaints.

Except for one! This one seed had been bored at first by all the bad vibrations around him, then genuinely annoyed, and now he knew that if he paid any more attention to them, he would become just like them—a complainer who would never, ever grow.

So what if the rains wouldn't stop, and the sun hadn't come out. It was time to do something about it. All the others were waiting for something to happen outside themselves. Maybe nothing ever happened out there. Was there a sun? He had never seen it.

Their Great Legend was that the sun would come again. It had come once before, so the ancestral story went, and when it had all of "those-who-had-bloomed-before" had burst their jackets and raised their heads to heaven.

Now despair was rampant in the seeds like a fungus, corroding the very spirit of The Wanderer at the center of their beings.

Except for the one seed. The time had come to *do* something, and none of the others had thought of that. It had had enough of rain and mud too. Perhaps the thing to do was to *bring* the sun out.

Making a mighty effort of will, the seed slowly pushed out a small root. "Lord," it thought, "this is hard work!"

The other seeds were full of scorn. What good was it to try to amount to anything when the sun wasn't out. All of them knew the seed would come to a bad end. "Never start anything unless things are just right," was an old seed law.

Well, the single seed sent its root down, and in just a day it had a firm grip on Mother Earth. Instead of gripping, the other seeds went back to griping. "If only—" was the prelude to each of their thoughts.

The next day was rich with clouds, as full and fluffy as the cream topping on a shortcake. Not a ray of sun could get through, if there was a sun at all.

But the seed had forgotten now about "out there." It was engaged in a fierce concentration of all its powers of will and all its collective memory of what it was like to be born. It no longer knew of the other seeds, or the field, or the rain that continued to beat down. Deep within itself, the sun was being centered. The seed was giving birth to the sun.

The next day a green shoot burst abruptly through the roof of the seed, and bore the jacket up above the ground with it.

Just at that moment, above the field the clouds parted and a gorgeous sun appeared. The rest of the seeds were all dead and could not see it, but it was as beautiful as the Great Legend had said it would be. It wore a gown of golden light, and was crowned with a halo of pure white light.

The seed sent a shiver of warmth blossoming down its length from tip to root, then gathered itself and surged upwards towards the sun. For the seed had learned the Great Secret of the universe, that all along the sun had been shining within.

Primer for "The Seed's Secret"

According to most theories of psychology and sociology, each of us acts just the way he or she was programmed in life. That is, we first get a genetic programming from our parents, and this *determines* how we will behave in life, whether or not we will be sickly or strong, ambitious or lazy, brilliant or dull. Then our society and environment gives us another programming that goes on for the rest of our lives. According to the "Behaviorists," who formed their theories by studying rats and then applied them to man, our conduct is as predictable as rats in a maze, or rats in a trap, for so seems their philosophy of man.

Seeds can be studied in the same way. But how many of us have known persons who were terribly handicapped in some way; yet they eventually made more of their lives than those who were not. By following a regimen of diet and exercise, the sickly child can become strong, and the dull child by applying diligence can accomplish more than the brilliant one to whom things come easily, but who squanders his talent. The missing factor in the equations of the Behaviorists is an intangible, and that is why they do not include it, which is not to say that it does not exist. This intangible used to be called "will." No matter that it is not popular today, the point is that those who have it do not wait around for things to be right in the world "out there." Instead they make things right in their own heads, which very often seems to set things aright out there. But they must *will* change before it can take place. Changing themselves, they change the world. The predisposition to change, to evolve, may be found in the archetype of the Self.

"The Seed's Secret" is about a seed that knew that the sun is within. Jungians call this sun the Self. The way to Selfhood, or new birth, begins with a desire for change and an act of will. After that—all things are possible. As I said in the primer for "The Dream Castle," the Self is a God-image. It may also be thought of as a point, that is, the very center of the psyche. In *Two Essays on Analytical Psychology,* Jung states that "it might equally be called the 'God within us.' The beginnings of our whole psychic life seem inextricably rooted in this point, and all our highest and ultimate purposes seem to be striving towards it."

The Self may be likened also to God in the definition of Meister Eckhart: "God is an intelligible sphere whose circumference is nowhere and whose center is everywhere." For as well as being the center, the Self is also the "circumference" of the psyche, encompassing the ego, even though the ego resists recognizing anything greater than itself. Using an analogy from astronomy, I like to think of the Self as an expanding universe. The center of this universe is a *point* of infinitely powerful energy, but the outermost *boundaries* of this expanding universe are part of the same universe; thus, the Self is the psyche's center and its totality.

Basically the ego resists psychic growth, whereas the Self insists upon it. Those who say they do not dream are of course those who live lives dominated by the ego, resisting whatever messages may come from the Self into consciousness to promote and transform consciousness. Since the ego evolves out of the Self—and not vice-versa—the ego has a kind of inferiority complex for which it overcompensates by attempting to usurp and displace the kingly or God-like aspect of the Self.

As I said in "The Dream Castle" primer, dreams are "pathways, adventurous trails, yellow-brick-roads to higher consciousness." Selfhood, attaining one's highest potential, is the goal of Jungian psychology, Selfhood being the ideal end of the individuation process. Selfhood implies a kind of spiritual purpose in life, which advocates of reductive psychologies regard as mystical—or at the very least—unrealistic. However, as it seems that humanity collectively has been evolving towards a higher purpose, the trail thereto has been indicated and then blazed by those individuals willing to risk all in order to attain the loftiest of goals. The trail of human evolution is littered with failures, but when greatness is achieved in one life, it points the way for all to follow through the Great Individual's example of Selfhood.

But just as the Great Individuals, the heroes of mythology and history, pose threats to the established social order, so too the ego seeks to preserve what it takes to be its autonomy, its psychic advantage, its personal weal, against the psyche's Great Individual, the Self, who comes like a hero to topple the psychic status-quo. Traditional psychology says, "Make the individual suit the society, tailor-made to its needs, make him fit in as an integer unremarkable from his fellow men." From the point of view of Jungian psychology, which *is* the point of view of the Self, individuation may set the Self against the ego, as the Great Individual against society, if either resists transformation. For the ego has struggled from the dark depths of unconsciousness to attain what it takes to be its advantage and does not yield easily to the Self, which seeks a sacred marriage or reconciliation of conscious and unconscious, in order that there may be psychic balance and wholeness.

Thus the ego, when confronted by the goads to growth of the Self, must make choices which will abort or bring about individuation. However, without utilization of will, nothing can be accomplished. What then can make us harken to the Self's higher urgings to evolve, to individuate? Simply this: the knowledge, the wisdom, the ultimate intuition that we are each responsible for our own fate.

This wisdom is the seed's secret, "that all along the sun had been shining within." The sun being an apt symbol of the Self, as are also star, light, and circles, indicating completion of the psyche, we see in our story an "individuated" seed, a seed in which the urgings of the Self, acting through the seed, save it from the fate of other seeds, complainers all, who had to have things "just right" in order to flourish. And so in our lives, for the most part, we find excuses for our failures, never willing to face the fact that we ourselves wield the hand of fate. Becoming a Self, therefore, is like becoming the one seed in the pack (society) that blooms (fulfills its potential) even under the most adverse conditions. In the Gnostic *Gospel of Eve* we read:

> I stood on a lofty mountain and saw a mighty Man, and another, a dwarf, and heard as it were a voice of thunder, and drew nigh for to hear; and it spake unto me and said: "I am thou and thou are I; and wheresoever thou art I am there and I am sown (or scattered) in all; from whencesoever thou willest thou gatherest Me, and gathering Me thou gatherest Thyself."

The foregoing esoteric parable has a relation to "The Seed's Secret," for the essence of the mighty Man that is "sown in all" is the God-Self, or that essentially divine center in ourselves that seeks to return to divine unity ("gathering Me thou gatherest Thyself"). The Buddhists say, "Thou Art That," that is, one with the divine Creator. In our story, the Creator is called the Wanderer, and He has left in each seed "His Own Light." Thus, each of us has the potential for Selfhood; yet in our tale only one seed makes the right choice and activates his will, knowing "that if he paid any more attention to them, he would become just like them—a complainer who would never, ever grow." Choosing not to be concerned with conditions outside himself, in which all the other seeds were complaining in chorus, he takes the crucial step towards individuation, becoming an individual. This process involves centering, going within, where the seed is sustained by his myth of the Great Legend that "the sun would come again." The seed's Great Legend involves a kind of resurrection, since "all of 'those-who-had-bloomed-before' had burst their jackets and raised their heads to heaven."

By centering in the myth that the sun would come again, the seed has brought the sun within, Selfhood, and stilled the ego voices of the other seeds whose despair corroded "the very spirit of the Wanderer at the center of their beings." Ego demands have dominated the other seeds, snuffing out the spark of Selfhood.

The seed's next step involves an act of will, for centroversion (centering) alone cannot fulfill the potentials of Selfhood. Having actualized the sun within, the seed can now manifest the sun without, that is, in its sky. And so the clouds part, and the seed surges upwards to unite with its light.

Since the Self is the most important archetype in Jungian psychology, being a "God-image," and since it is the most rarely encountered in dreams, I think it may be helpful to present some further examples of the Self's symbology in order that it be recognized. Gold is the metal identified with the sun, and gold, diamonds, the philosopher's stone, symbols of preciousness, are all indicative of the Self. Further, a fantastic human figure or animal may symbolize the Self. The sun is the center of our solar system, and dream symbology involving circles or centers indicates the psyche's turn towards centroversion. Because the Self has divine implications, symbology connected with heights, the heavens, or stars and lights therein, as well as the general theme of ascent, may indicate the psyche's aspiration towards its divine component. Lastly, symbology involving children, babies, and birth in general, suggests the psyche's dissatisfaction with "the old life" and its desire to bring about a new birth of consciousness. Jung has written extensively on the latter symbology in "On Rebirth" and "The Child Archetype" in volume nine of his collected works, *The Archetypes and the Collective Unconscious*.

In conclusion, for those readers who may not have experienced as yet any Big Dreams, their occurrence coinciding with life changes as a result of inner transformations of consciousness, I would like to share a Big Dream about the Self. I am in a bookstore, a source of wisdom to those of us who read. For the purpose of calling attention to the dream's important elements, I shall italicize them. Similar to Field's Bookstore in San Francisco, the books go all the way to a very *high* ceiling. Since I am tall (6′3″), I am able to reach—by stretching—one of the highest books, and I take it down from the shelf and look for a place to read.

The *center* of the store contains a *round* leather seat that surrounds a *pole* reaching from the center of the circular seat to the *top* of the ceiling. I sit down and open the book. Next to me on the round seat is a *baby,* left unattended while her parents evidently browse the shelves. The book contains very realistic and beautiful pictures of nature scenes, such as those published by the Sierra Club. Fascinated, I watch as the trees bend to an invisible wind, and clouds move from one border of the page across the picture, disappearing as they pass into the next border. "What magical book is this?" I think. I hold it with great reverence and awe. The child has been looking at the pages as I turn them, and now begins to remove them, one at a time. I fear the child will harm the book, but it puts the pages back in the book, but in a different order.

When I awaken, I have the feeling of having participated in a mystery revelation. For days thereafter, I experience quiet rapture. Communicating the dream to a psychic friend of mine, she tells me, "The Book of Nature is being opened to you, and its mysteries revealed. The child is the Self that teaches you that nature has a different order and reality than that which ordinarily appears. Beneath the visible forms, are laws that correspond more to magic than physics, for the Self creates the forms of life."

And so, our Big Dreams may be the Self dreaming! Suddenly our ordinary lives seem enhanced, fraught with new meaning, part of a greater plan that seems to transcend the mundane world. The "plan" of each psyche is designed by the Self, in the same way that the kernel of a seed contains the potential for a majestic oak in a tiny acorn.

Peg Kranz © 1982

TRAVELS WITH MOZART

Last night I was sitting before my radio listening to music and musing on the idea that everything in the universe possesses consciousness. Of course, communicating with animals and insect life presents no problems. It is a simple matter of telepathy and they are "sending" all the time. With the vegetable kingdom it is more difficult. They may receive one's emotions for some time before deciding to reveal their own.

With the mineral kingdom the best way is through touch. What is received is not yet differentiated into emotion or thought as we know it, but a subtle system of vibrations is present. A little red smooth stone that has spent the last two millions years of its life in the bed of a crystalline mountain stream may beat with a pulse like a salmon's heart. Indeed, he may have been many times part of the walls of salmons' nests, and when he has graduated from his next grade—the vegetable kingdom—one can be assured that he will head for the water once more, probably as a salmon.

Naturally, a stone in the desert has quite a different pulse. Eons baking under a relentless sun have taught him to conserve his vibrations. He must, or shatter into dust as many of his own chips off the old block had done. Why only yesterday in the Paleolithic era there had been a whole family of rocks around him. As he gets older, he seems to live more and more in the past, along with his "memories" and the indefatigable sun.

So you see everything possesses consciousness. Consciousness uses matter to dress up the way we put on clothes to suit our moods. Indeed, my own thoughts have no sooner flown from my head than they are out there somewhere in the universe putting on clothes and starting worlds of their own, but that is another tale and needs forever in the telling.

I was listening to the W. Mozart Sonata for Flute and Harpsichord when I began to wonder where the notes go when they leave the radio. Holden Caulfield was concerned with where the Central Park ducks went in the winter. I found my question much more interesting, and for a while sat transfixed as the notes poured over my head and shoulders in a melodic shower. Given that everything has consciousness, what was the consciousness of an individual note and where did it go once it came out of the radio? And, also, if a thousand people were listening to the same station at the same time, would the same note go to the same place from each of the radios?

Of course, the physicists would say that notes just die, as they say we die. This nonsense keeps the churches at least partially filled, and makes one wonder if the scientists are not in the employ of the churches instead of on opposite sides of the fence.

At any rate, to discover the consciousness of a note I had to think back on the chain of its life. The radio was in part responsible for its being borne to me. Here was a contraption that I still didn't understand. Imagine my radio dialed to another station. The Mozart sonata doesn't exist! Or rather it does exist like a chain of notes flying like wild geese in formation in the moon-struck sky above my city. I dial the right station and the geese dive down into my radio and come out but to where? To my ears, of course, but that is not right either. A note does exist in at least two dimensions at the same time. It goes out somewhere and simultaneously goes into my ear and becomes a part of my consciousness—swallowed, so to speak. But I can't swallow all of a note. If I could then others in the room could not hear the note, and even if all the ears in the world were waiting by my radio to swallow the note, somehow that note would escape for its solitary flight to infinity. No, to solve the mystery I would have to go back further than the radio for the birth of the note. All right, what about the station? Better—but they are only playing a record. The birth of the record—indelible in plastic? Nope, one has to get back further. The orchestra playing the sonata that will be a record that the station will play that I will hear if I tune in to the right place in space and time? You see, now there are almost infinite probabilities involved in anything we do. In a sense the orchestra creates the sonata that I will hear, but the real source is Mozart, isn't it? One can see him in his dusty studio—he was always a poor housekeeper—manuscripts piled to the ceiling, prolific as a bee in clover time.

All right, now I've got it. Or have I? After all, the sonata's notes are not ground out of Mozart's brain like sausage from a meat grinder. No, we don't know very much about the brain, let alone where it leaves off and mind begins.

Psychology might say that the sonata already exists in Mozart's collective unconscious, but where did Mozart's unconscious begin, if not with the first man, and again, where did the notes' consciousness begin? If they came before Mozart, one can imagine the sonata waiting to waylay Mozart once he had rattled off the cosmic assembly line. "Get it together, Wolfgang, I've been waiting a long time."

It was no good wondering where the notes went when they left the radio when I could not decide where they came from in the first place. And Holden thought he had problems!

Obviously, logic and intellect were failing in this problem, as they always seem to do in the most important questions.

Then intuition told me that the place where the notes went to was the same place that they came from. Of this I was certain, but it really didn't tell me anymore. Then, like a flash from the blue, the answer came to me. The only way to know where the notes go is to go there with them! For this I would have to make my consciousness very small and then somehow get inside a note as it came out of the radio. It is simply a matter of focus. Imagine a gigantic microscope with many lenses of varied powers. From afar, the Earth might appear to be like a single molecule, and its consciousness all of a kind. Then if the power is stepped up by switching to a higher lens, perhaps all of New York can be seen. Flip to another lens, and we may see one block on the upper West Side. The consciousness is different with each power. The first was human consciousness, the second New York, and the third an amalgamation of black, Jewish, and Puerto Rican, with a sprinkling of old Irish.

But when you monkey around with spatial dimensions, funny things may happen with time. The focus on that New York City block might turn out to be all Dutch, or even all Indian, or all underwater. Space/time is fluid.

My own consciousness had been focused in what I took to be the Now. For telling me where the notes went, the Now was Nowhere; so I mentally flipped lenses in my head until I could perceive the notes dancing out of the radio.

I wasn't prepared for what I saw; I thought they would be all the same. Fat notes, slender, reedy notes, silver, all passing by. All going somewhere! They were like a parade, or a flying circus!

E. GILL

The moment had arrived to get inside a note. Suddenly I saw the one I wanted. I'm sure it just had been played by a flute because it very much resembled a long platinum space ship, and had portholes in its sides like the valve openings in a flute. Also I think it was an F major note, but there is no way to verify this. Seeing my chance, I directed all of my consciousness into one of the open portholes, and found myself safely inside.

To my surprise, I wasn't alone. Like New York, or the Earth molecule, this note was not of just one consciousness at all. Oh, there were many others along for the ride. Some I recognized as half-notes, and their poor country relations the quarter notes. Others had different harmonics and vibrations to them, and appeared in very strange costumes. Others were more shadowy—there one moment and not the next, phasing in and out like a winking neon sign. I suspected they did double duty—or more—in other systems elsewhere in the universe. Imagine the same note being used in other symphonies, other concertos, in other systems of the universe *at the same time!*

I thought of looking out the porthole I had come in, and saw myself immobile before the radio as the space note gradually moved past. Then very strange things appeared as I looked out the window. It was like looking at innumerable scrolls on which a multitude of scenes were being projected. One very meaningful scene was myself as a baby taking my first steps. I remembered the scene because my father had captured the moment on film, and this tableau was exactly like that except for being of a different angle than that of the movie. My mother was there, down on her haunches, her hands extended in encouragement, and I laughing as I raced/fell towards her.

But this scene was only one of billions taking place—one that I recognized, although somehow I felt that I had been involved with all the others too. There were also images of probabilities of myself as an old man. These "scenes" were not on flat areas like movie screens or canvases. It was as if billions of banners were whirling outside the window, and on each a riot of movement that might dwindle completely as the "banner" narrowed at its end, only to have the scene reappear again at a new angle in relation to the original plane. On some the action ran backwards, or back then forward and back. All of them interacted at more angles and on more planes than my consciousness was capable of comprehending. Some were seen along the edges of their planes. And all of them were transparent so that there was seemingly no behind or no to-the-fore, no up and no down. Thus they could all be viewed simultaneously.

Though this fascinated my consciousness, it knew that it would be lost out there, and drew back, as does a man on a skyscraper who looks too long at the ground and suddenly sees it jump up at him; then loses his balance and falls.

I centered myself again inside the note and purposely did not look out again. After a time, the "ship" passed through some kind of screen that gave the appearance of slowly moving down from the front to the back. It was like a net that caught some of the half notes and other passengers, and did strange things to them. As they encountered this barrier, their shapes warped and flattened, refracting along angles perpendicular to the ship.

Ahead I could still see the very beginning of the note, now vacant of any passengers besides myself. As the note continued to pass through it and the barrier moved towards me, I realized that it was a membrane separating the space/time system I had been in from another. The other passengers used this cosmic interchange to get off because their destination was not the same as my own.

I was going some place where everything that I had known would no longer apply.

I wondered if ground control could abort this mission now, but I felt no connection anymore with the stonelike form of myself that I had seen out of the porthole eons ago. After a time—although the rules of time no longer applied either—there was a gap, a blackness in my consciousness. Finally, a jolt as if the note had finally come to rest.

I looked out and saw a vast, dazzling white extending to infinity. On it were evenly spaced lines. Perhaps this is Mars and the *canali,* I thought. I changed my focus. I saw that the note rested at the end of a giant phallus that extended far up into the sky. Suddenly, behind a glass, an eye appeared at the end of the phallus. I felt like an atom, or amoeba, or a molecule under a microscope. The eye peered closer, and a face wearing spectacles formed about it. It was Mozart! I would recognize him anywhere. The phallus came down on the white plane and the note was squeezed out. This was its beginning, its birth, inserted between the first and second lines of the white plane by Mozart's quill pen. Then I read Mozart's instructions on the musical staff. I was right, it was an F major!

Suddenly Mozart muffed it. Perhaps it was my being there, or perhaps the note's own consciousness muffed it, but it dribbled below the bar, then compounded this in an unsightly mess. I saw the gigantic hand of genius reaching for the page, closing down upon us. We were like sinners in the hand of an angry god. We were crumbled, my note and I, then lifted and borne towards the flames. We were not going to make it to the same system again.

As we fluttered down into the fire, I felt a shudder in my note's whole being. Alchemically, the ink was reacting to the fire and I knew we were going to a far, far better world. There would be new membranes to traverse, new worlds to conquer for my note and me. If you want some inkling of where we are now, turn this page up and read along the edge. . . .

Primer for "Travels with Mozart"

This story is about imagination. Imagination is lighter than a feather and faster than light, because anyone can be anywhere at any time. Imagination is made fun of by grown-ups, but never by Jungian grown-ups because they know that what they don't know is more than they do know, which most grown-ups don't know.

All the great accomplishments of mankind—the inventions, scientific formulae, all the works of art—existed first in imagination. One day a man may travel by mind alone to other stars and planets, returning again to tell what he has seen and heard on his fantastic voyage.

Tomorrow the human race will be different from what it is today. We are changing and it is the mind that is changing our bodies and our world. The active imagination process is a way of "tripping" without drugs. Thinking in new ways releases chemical molecules that reprogram the brain. Thinking new thoughts, therefore, creates a new brain, that sends us tripping in a way that is absolutely fail safe.

But mind is divided into two parts, the conscious mind, and the unconscious or sleeping mind. When we go into the unconscious mind, we find that it is "awake" because of all the activity we find there—the many events and people. Indeed, there is so much going on there that we can remember only very little when we awaken. Things move so slowly in the conscious mind that it seems from the point of view of the unconscious mind that the dreamer has fallen asleep when he leaves the unconscious to "wake up." The conscious mind is so suspicious of the unconscious that it will say things like "that was nothing but a dream," or "it's only your imagination." Though seemingly always at odds, the two minds are like an old married couple that live on just to be together. Jungians want both minds to have a real marriage, for the conscious mind needs the intuitions and feelings of the unconscious if it is to be anything more than half a mind.

The way Jungians explore the unconscious is called "active imagination." This means that one can dream a dream while awake, so that what is happening can be followed. When one recalls such a "dream" later, it will tell you much about yourself, where you go, and what you want to be. You can guide it yourself, or have someone you trust go along with you as your guide. You are exploring what the conscious mind regards as strange country, but this process is one of the best ways to accomplish the marriage and brings the two minds together.

According to Jung in volume 18 of his collected works, there is a difference between active imagination and fantasy: "A fantasy is more or less your own invention, and remains on the surface of personal things and conscious expectations. But active imagination, as the term denotes, means that the images have a life of their own and that the symbolic events develop according to their own logic—that is, of course, if your conscious reason does not interfere."

As to the value of active imagination, we can perhaps say that the more difficult it is for one to do, the more valuable the time spent permitting the unconscious mind to come into consciousness. Why? Because one who is too highly intellectual—too *conscious*—is in a state of psychic imbalance in which the unconscious contents are discredited as nonsense whenever they may surface in consciousness. Or, in some cases, the conscious mind has created a barrier against the unconscious, as in persons who announce proudly, "I don't dream."

As to the method of active fantasy, Jung tells us, "When you concentrate on a mental picture, it begins to stir, the image becomes enriched by details, it moves and develops. . . . And so when we concentrate on an inner picture and when we are careful not to interrupt the natural flow of events, our unconscious will produce a series of images which make a complete story." (*The Tavistock Lectures: On the Theory and Practice of Analytical Psychology,* vol. 18, p. 172.)

The preceding is a "complete story" which my unconscious gave to me by active imagination, a trip I took with Mozart's music into another dimension of time and space. Try giving your own imagination free reign. You may be surprised how it takes on a life of its own—just as the unconscious has a creative life of its own, independent of the conscious mind.

THE CRYSTAL PEOPLE

Once upon a very long time ago there was a race on earth called the Crystal People. They looked very much like you and I except in the center of their foreheads there grew out an inch or two a cluster of beautiful crystals.

If you were up close to these people, you could see little tiny figures in the crystals, a king and queen perhaps, or a wise old man or woman. And all of them seemed to have at least one disagreeable figure, dark and shadowy, which when called to the attention of that person was always denied. Why that was so, I could not say, except that no one would want to admit to having such a nasty character in the middle of his head.

Now the very strange thing about these people was that you could tell what they were seeing only by examining the little figures in their heads. What happened was this. As they turned to look at someone or something, one of the little figures in the crystal would fall into place at the center, from which a light of brilliant intensity emitted. So at the same moment that the object was seen, the light fell upon it, cloaking it in the garb of the king of queen, or the nasty, shadowy person, turning a boulder into a troll, or a weeping willow into a stick-riding witch, hair trailing down clouds as she flew on a mission of witchery.

Strangest of all was the way these people fell in love, for seemingly the most important figure for this was an image of the opposite sex that each possessed in his or her crystal. Oddly enough these tiny figures when projected outward became larger than life. Too, they were not always ideal objects for love, since some of them seemed to find attractive what others found unattractive.

For example, one man might have an image of a naked beauty, young, savage, and unevolved, but another's "beauty" more nearly resembled his grandmother, with whitening hair and a figure in need of immediate repair. If questioned about this, the man might say, "I prefer a more mature woman." Thus in looking at a young woman, she might come to resemble his grandmother, and in time he would begin to scold his love for not being "what I thought you were."

By far the greatest number of these figures—for both men and women—were romantic figures from the past and the future. Although the Crystal People lived eons before the race of men on earth, there, sure enough, in their heads were Helen of Troy, Cleopatra, and other great lovers yet to walk the earth. And our gods and goddesses were already in their heads: Apollo, Zeus, Diana, chaste goddess of the Moon, and Athena, Greek goddess of wisdom.

So it seemed that whatever quality a man or woman deemed important for his or her own fulfillment, he was sure to project a figure onto his beloved that embodied that quality, whether from past or future. How this was possible I cannot say; yet as these images contained gods and goddesses from the race of men, there were also great figures of imagination from the race of men, and stranger figures, whom I did not know, but whose meaning came to me by the feeling they gave.

Imagine, if you will, a Crystal maiden, comely in every feature, and lithesome of limb, pursued by many suitors, and yet unable to love anyone more than momentarily, for in her head was the image of Don Juan, that great and faithless lover of Byron's, symbol in human history of the unregenerate seducer. And there he was in the Crystal maiden's head, thousands of years before Byron would create him, an image waiting to be actualized, and so projected each day by the maiden onto a local lord or bumpkin whom she would play false.

And so love's sighs were heard everywhere in this land, and minstrels were in great demand. Gatherings of musicians were mobbed, for the singers of love often became the objects of love when the projection was turned upon them, and the kinds of songs they sang were as varied as the figures in the heads of the Crystal People. Here one group clustered about half-savage men and women clad only in animal skins and bird feathers, who beat upon drums, pots and pans, and each other, creating a caterwauling that accompanied posturings suggesting the throes of sexual ecstasy. The audiences, of course, reflected the performers, both in appearance and performance, for the audience gyrated and writhed with the cacophony that came from the stage.

Less popular were sweet singers who sang of love's pain to the accompaniment of lute-like instruments, while some in the audience fainted or wept as each note of unrequited love resonated on their heart strings.

Still rarer were small groups that gathered to hear musicians and singers play a kind of intricate, mathematical counterpoint such as might marry the theories of Einstein and the intricacies of a fourth dimension Johann Sebastian Bach. In this music, what we might call the music of the spheres, the listener was transported to rarified, spiritual realms ruled by gods and goddesses commensurate with the images carried within his head. Curious, was it not, that these ancient Crystal People, not unlike our own race, found in music the levels of ecstasy to accompany the procession of images that played within their heads?

Sadly, those who bore the most evolved figures within their crystals, figures that seemed embodiments or abstractions of the highest human traits, faced almost certain disenchantment when the projections lit upon the ordinary folk of their village. For if Minerva's mantle of wisdom were thrown over the shoulders of a country milkmaid, it would not be very long before the muddy toes of clay would begin to protrude beneath the sacred hem of sagacity.

Fortunately, among some of these there was a kind of awakening to the realization that the qualities projected were within the crystal images—which they could not see themselves—and not in the persons onto whom they were projected. This led ultimately to a kind of introversion within these persons, so that they sought salvation not so much from their fellows as from the capacity to create for themselves the qualities they desired for fulfillment. This process had amazing results! As they personally became more whole, they demanded less of others, but what is more, through their own fulfillment they were able to see others as they really were. By accepting them as they were, the process of disenchantment did not take place, and these persons had relations that lasted as long as a lifetime.

For myself, I was ready to test the way in which the crystals worked by personally observing the projections in action. It was not long before a young princess came stepping down the path, while humming softly to herself of her "true love." I spoke to her about whom she quested (a prince, of course), when she cried out, "Oh, here he comes now! My true love, riding a white horse." As I looked in the direction of her gaze, I saw a large green bullfrog, hopping towards us. As he reached the pond, by whose edge we sat, he dove in and disappeared from view. Clutching her hands to her bosom she sighed, "For me he'd swim the deepest ocean."

Gazing into her crystal, I saw the prince she sought, but having fixed her eyes on the poor hoptoad, the transformation of it for her was complete. Fortunate, thought I, that we humans are not as deceived as the Crystal People.

I was about to take my leave of the princess when she fell into the pool and was drowned, I feared, for she never appeared again. Sadly I rose and started down the path to a new adventure, when I saw one of their wise old men straddling an oaken stump. "Sir," he said, "the ways of men must be strange indeed, for the past half hour I have heard you converse with a frog."

Primer for "The Crystal People"

In "The Crystal People," I have removed the archetypes from the unconscious and placed them "out-front," so to speak. In this manner we are able to observe the effects of the projection of the archetypes. Our way of seeing others is conditioned by the specific qualities of our archetypes. For although the quantity of the archetype is the same in each of us—a prince is a prince is a prince is a prince—the *quality* of that archetype is unique for each of us; thus by merely observing another person, in effect we have projected our quality of the archetype onto that person.

Since there cannot be a strictly objective observer, Heisenberg's Uncertainty Principle in physics is paralleled by Jung's awareness that merely looking is highly subjective, clothing the object or person in the qualitative garb of our own archetypal projections. Good, evil, love, hate—these qualities we assign to people at first meetings, often even before a word is spoken. "I hated the man at once." Or, "it was a case of love at first sight." Such strong reactions *before* the other person is known at all indicate that the unconscious archetype has been aroused by the other person and its *quality* projected onto him.

My story is perhaps an unconscious take-off on the Grimm classic "The Frog Prince." In that tale, we may recall, the prince had been turned into a frog by some spell or enchantment by a witch. From the point of view of Jungian psychology, the projection-making quality of the unconscious is a kind of enchantment, for the other person taking the projection appears to be someone he is not. When two persons establish an intense relation based upon such a projection, we can predict that they are headed for trouble, since neither sees the other as he or she really is, and "disenchantment" is sure to follow.

Jung's psychology, which may have seemed mystical and impractical in regard to the Self, becomes quite down-to-earth in regard to the give and take of the war between the sexes. Indeed, I would say that Jung's most important contributions to psychology are in the area of sexual relations.

One purpose of Jungian psychology is to make us aware of our projections in order to be able to see others as they really are, for in many cases we find ourselves disappointed because others do not fulfill our *expectations* of them. Thus, a kind of disenchantment takes place, and we blame others for our unfulfilled expectations, saying, "You are not what I thought you were."

The more we explore our Dream Castle, the unconscious mind, the more we are aware of the qualities of our own archetypes, catching ourselves in the act of projecting. Naturally when one falls in love, some projection has occurred; otherwise the individual singled out as the source of our enchantment would not stand out from all the rest. When we see this happen to one of our friends we say, "I wonder what he sees in her." When it happens to us, we are quite sure the object of our love has special qualities others do not possess. The narrator of our story is capable of seeing that his "young princess" is in love with a frog, but is not able to see that she herself is a frog.

So the crystals in the foreheads of the Crystal People are metaphors of the projection-making quality of the archetypes. In the matter of love, each of us longs for completion by a polar opposite, the *anima* in men, and the *animus* in women. Let us call them Miss Right and Mr. Right. When Mr. and Miss Right turn out to be Mr. and Miss Wrong as is usually the case, we can be sure that a projection of archetypes of *anima* and *animus* has been involved in our initial enchantment and subsequent disenchantment.

Dreams of the *animus* and *anima* are quite common, particularly from puberty onwards, since they are associated initially with sexual development. Indeed, recent studies of dreaming subjects have determined that during a night's sleep both sexes experience many periods of sexual arousal. During such times, we may imagine that the import of the dream is of a sexual nature.

Analysis of the way that Mr. or Miss Right appear to the dreamer is of extreme importance because it is a direct reflection of the archetypal level of development of the animus or anima. That is, one can determine the particular quality of his anima or her animus, and this knowledge will reveal the reason behind one's attraction to a certain type. At the same time, the level of development of the animus or anima is a valuable clue to the overall development of the psyche, whether or not one is on the path of individuation, for example, or whether one seems stuck, repeating past patterns of conduct that have led to disappointment, frustration, and regret.

To give an example, animus and anima have been categorized according to four levels of development, which proceed as follows:

1) The animus/a appear as seductive sexual figures, or as objects or animals to which the dreamer finds himself attracted. Often the figure arousing the dreamer is elusive, but just as often some sort of sexual relation is consummated. Now on this primary level, sexual release is all that is sought. Yet such dreams beyond puberty and the teen years, may indicate that the dreamer views the opposite sex as sex objects, serving the purpose of sexual release, but with whom there is no real relation as *persons*.

2) The second level contains much of the sexual attraction of the first level, but now love comes into the picture, and with it, caring, for now such dreams reveal the psyche's desire for its other half, completion through relation. Animus/a dreams of Mr. or Miss Right have a profound effect when recalled upon awakening. One is still in love, but with whom one knows not as the dream vision begins to vanish in the light of day. And when we fall in love, life becomes like a dream vision, the world illumined by enchantment. Such dreams indicate that the dreamer seeks fulfillment not from within, in the realm of the Self, but from another person without; hence such longing is usually doomed.

3) Continual failure and disenchantment may lead to a partial centering in the psyche, which may end the period of waiting for another to set the life right. Thereupon, one may begin to dream of men or women who *inspire,* releasing creative energies which the psyche had squandered earlier upon sexual relations. The man's muse or the woman's teacher may reconnect the conscious mind to unconscious sources that begin to fulfill the Self's urgings toward higher development.

4) The final stage of animus or anima development, although rarely attained, confers *wisdom,* a knowledge of personal relation to our world and universe, and our own unique place in the scheme of things. And, ultimately, this level is the end of projection, for whatever guru we may have instructing us now warns that the projection is to be fully withdrawn, that the divinity we see in them is to be found in none other than ourself. Thus animus and anima guard the last threshold to Selfhood, for until we have passed this portal we cannot find divinity within, indi-

viduation, or total integration of consciousness and unconscious archetypes. As long as this crucial archetype is projected, like Sleeping Beauty we await rescue from without. But oddly enough, when we have found our purpose in life, are deep in creative endeavors, and aware of our particular relation to the world, then Fate (aha, ourselves!) brings along Mr. or Miss Right just when we no longer *need* them. Not needing their love, we can give our own in an unconditional way, thereby insuring the success of our relation with them, although unable, perhaps, to resist a final question: "Where were you when I needed you?!"

E.GILL

THE FOUR RINGS

There were once three brothers who lived with their father the king on the nethermost boundaries of the world, where light leaves off and darkness begins. His kingdom was very great, and when all three of his sons had come of age, he called them to him, and said, "My sons, the time has come to promise my kingdom. One of you shall claim it all, the other two shall receive nothing. Unknown to you, you have a step-sister placed under an enchantment at her christening by my sister, Queen Darkness, Witch of the South, who was regrettably excluded from the christening. Since that day, your sister has never awakened, but sleeps under a deep spell of unconsciousness. Yet she has grown ever more beautiful, and will love forever the one who awakens her. He shall have my kingdom and riches, and his step-sister shall be his bride."

The next day, the three brothers mounted their horses and rode away with heavy hearts, for each feared the loss of the kingdom. The two eldest brothers rode north together, seeking that way to support one another, and thus to avoid the dark and dangerous kingdom of their aunt, the Witch of the South. But the youngest brother, reasoning that his step-sister would be in the south, rode ever towards the sun, watching it rise over his left shoulder by day, and set below his right shoulder at night.

After many days he came to where the plateau of his father's kingdom began to drop off in a long descent towards the floor of a valley which marked the beginning of the domain of Queen Darkness. Heat waves rippled over the valley's sands, and no breeze stirred the air, nor was water to be found anywhere. Presently his horse stopped from thirst and would go no further. His own flask was empty. Dismounting, he led the horse along by the rein, when suddenly a well appeared from nowhere. Before he could drink, an old woman barred his path.

"Would you drink from my well?" asked the old woman.

"If you grant it," said the young brother.

"These waters will make you very wise," said the old woman, "but only a fool would drink from this well."

"In that case, it is folly to be wise."

The old woman laughed at his words and moved with him to the well. "Do me one kindness, young man. I have lost my ring of lead in the well. It is of little worth by itself, but priceless with its fellows. Your arms are long and you could reach it for me. As you see, the well is not deep."

Peering in, he saw the ring lying a foot or so beneath the waters. "I'll hold your legs so you don't fall in," said the old woman.

The young man, whose name was Prince Parta, clambered over the well's wall and lowered his hands into the water. The ring was but inches from his fingertips.

"I'll have to put a little of my head in," said Parta.

"When you do," said the old woman, "slip a finger through the ring and I'll draw you up."

No sooner was his head beneath water than he saw the bottom was deeper than he thought. Nevertheless, with his head and shoulders completely under he was sure to reach it. Just then the ring seemed to move deeper. Lunging with one hand, he quickly passed his finger into its hole and prepared to draw it up. But the ring seemed to weigh a thousand times what a ring should weigh, and he felt himself being pulled deeper and deeper into the well, the bottom of which began to come up rapidly.

In the twinkling of an eye, he was stretched out on the floor of a flower-carpeted forest next to a well, the ring gone from his finger.

"Is this where the well comes out?" he wondered.

"This is the other side of the earth," said a serpent twined about the well. "Oh, dear, I'm afraid the ring has fallen to the very center."

"How shall I find the ring now?" despaired the Prince. "Well, no matter, my task is to find my sister. The old woman will have to find her ring by herself."

"Oh, no," said the serpent, uncoiling from the wall and slithering closer, "without this ring you cannot find your sister, and with it you cannot find your sister."

"That makes no sense at all," said Parta peevishly. "If you're going to be a talking serpent, the least you can do is make sense."

The serpent reared up in front of him to a full five feet, hissing menacingly. What a curious thing, thought Parta, the serpent has soft brown eyes like a human being.

Just at that moment, the old woman's head popped up at the edge of the well.

"Young man, do me the kindness of helping me out of this well. It's a long climb for such an old woman."

"You tricked me," said Parta. "You're better off in the well where you can do no more harm. I don't know where I am, and yet I must find my sister."

At this remark the serpent looked at Parta with such a pleading look that he walked to the well and hauled out the old woman.

"Well done," she said. "I have four riddles as your reward. Solve them and you save your sister."

"Save her!" said the Prince, startled. "Is she in danger?"

"Not unless you fail," said the woman.

"Let me see a riddle then."

From her pocket, the woman took a brown paper and read to him thusly:

" 'If you heed the serpent well,
You may find yourself in Hell.
There lies the ring of lead
Speaking both to damned and dead.' "

"Serpents speak with forked tongue," said the Prince, "and as for going to Hell, I'd as soon do that in my own time."

"Stubborn, stubborn," said the crone, climbing back into the well. "When you have won the ring of lead, you'll get the second riddle, but not before." So saying, she dropped from sight, and the Prince peered over the side and watched as she receded faster and faster from view.

The serpent had caught the riddle in its mouth as the crone dropped it on the ground, and now offered it to the Prince.

"It says the ring speaks both to damned and dead," puzzled the Prince. "That cannot be. Rings do not speak."

"Unless it lies under tongue," said the serpent. At this Parta grasped the snake beneath its head, prying apart its jaws with both hands, shaking it towards the ground, searching for the ring.

Upon releasing it, the serpent coughed and gasped, then hissed at Parta. "Had I the ring, I would have given it to you.

If you do not trust me, there is no hope of finding your bride and sister."

"And how do you know she is to be my bride, Speckled One?"

The serpent did not answer, but coiled itself once more about the well. Parta prepared to move on. He felt himself to be part of a wild goose chase, and would tarry no longer. Sensing his imminent departure, the serpent raised its head and spoke once more.

"I will take you to the ring, but alone it cannot help you find your bride. There are three others, and their magic works only when they are together."

"Take me there then," commanded Parta.

"You must prepare yourself, for we journey to the center of the earth. Gather grasses, and when you have returned with them, stuff up your nose, ears, and mouth, and cover your eyes."

When the Prince had returned and prepared himself as instructed, he grasped tightly the serpent's tail, and the serpent began to burrow into the earth.

It seemed to Parta that they had been moving for an eternity, when the serpent pushed through into an underground cavern, dragging Parta along behind. The serpent helped Parta remove the protective grasses from his head, and when he had opened his eyes, there lay before him a cavern of such vastness that the end was not in sight. Upon the walls and overhead danced black shadows, silhouetted by all shades of red, scarlet, and crimson, emitted from an ever-changing fire that seemed to dance in rhythm to the human shadows. The floor of the cavern was a vast pit in which the fires flowed, immersing as if in molten lava the poor human creatures that wallowed there, each chained to another, so that one's struggle to free himself from the fire only served to drag his fellow further in.

When Parta had unplugged his ears he wished at once that he had not, for the wailing and lamentation that assailed his ears was more horrible than the sight he beheld. Then to his nose came the stench of that suffering, as if each sin had bred its own unique corruption.

He drew back at once to the protection of the hole whence they had entered, but the serpent came to him and spoke.

"Fear not! You come here of your own free will. Nothing here can harm you. These shadows are not of your creation."

The serpent glided towards the edge of the pit of fire, Parta following, then hesitating at the edge.

"This fire was not created by yourself for your own punishment; hence it cannot harm you. Hold to my back and I shall guide you through."

They entered the fire and proceeded towards the center, which lay many miles ahead. Soon the creatures in the fire, desperate for rescue, sought to enfold them in their chains.

Again the serpent spoke to Parta in his peril. "Their chains are selfmade, for in life they forsook the will."

Overhead the shadows of crimson and black danced their gruesome *pas de deux,* as the serpent glided through the fire as if it were lava, Parta clinging to his back. After a time he became aware of another voice above the mass lamentation, and this voice came from the figure at the center towards which they made their way. Its upper body was hairy and blackened, and bore the semblance of a goat, gigantic horns sprouting from the forehead, upon which was emblazoned the fiery emblem of an inverted five-pointed star. The lower half of the body was scaly and dark green like either a fish or a serpent. Now Parta felt himself touched and caressed by the hands and bodies of alluring women who grasped at him as he passed by.

"Heed them not," said the serpent. "You carry your beloved with you always. They cannot dissuade you from your purpose."

"My purpose!" thought Parta. So great had been his fear and fascination that he had not thought of his sister since they had entered the cave. But the serpent's words had served to remind him of his Quest.

Now, as they drew nearer what seemed to be a throne on which the Goat-Serpent reclined, its coils ever moving, its tail thrashing angrily, Parta realized that it spoke to the miserable multitude in an unknown tongue.

"He does not speak to you," said the serpent. "That is why you cannot comprehend."

All at once Parta saw a sight that caused him greater agony than any he had yet seen. His two brothers, in chains near the base of the throne, called to him. He was about to leave the serpent's back and make for them, when the serpent spoke again.

"They are but the darker aspects of yourself, waiting to be liberated."

Then Parta and the serpent emerged from the lake of fire onto the throne of ice. Carefully avoiding the writhing coils, the serpent guided Parta to a safe place on the throne. Warning him not to move, the serpent began to climb the throne, where high above the strange tongue spoke to all but Parta. As the King of Evil spoke, the serpent wound about his neck and slithered slowly upward until, darting its head into that loathsome maw, it plucked out the ring of lead.

And at that moment precisely, the voice of the King of Evil spoke to Parta alone.

"The ring shall free and bind you at the same time!"

NOW LAND

When the serpent broke through to the surface of the earth, they were exactly at the same spot as before, but it seemed to Parta that the land was new, somehow transformed. There were things that he had looked at before, but never really seen. There was so much more to see!

The well was surrounded by luxuriant emerald green grasses and exotic flowers that made the spot a perpetual garden. Hollyhocks and lilies, all taller than a man, grew around the well, and in their gentle shade irises and orchids opened to a blue sky as vast and deep as an ocean. But for all the visual beauty of this marvelous garden, and the perfumes wafted by gentle zephyrs from the gaudy blooms, most pleasing to all the senses was the sound of delightful music no human ear had heard before.

From the depth of every blossom there welled up a sweet liquid that falling from tendril and leaf gave off sounds, perhaps like xylophones or harps or flutes, but more exotic and heavenly pitched, as if the music of the spheres had manifested in this floral orchestra. Tasting this ambrosia Parta found his mind reeling with visions of strange, fey creatures whom he knew at once to be the soul of each flower.

"Here the notes have wings and sing," said the serpent. And, indeed, as he watched, a flock of notes came flying in, roosting in the trees, and commencing to sing.

"I shall call this Now Land," said Parta, "for here one cares not for the past, nor is concerned with the future. To remain here forever is enough. If I could find a wife here that would be perfection."

"Do you forget your bride and sister so easily?" said the serpent.

"Ah, I had almost forgotten," said Parta sadly.

"Young man," called the crone, "give us a hand up." Parta turned and saw the head of the old woman pop up above the wall.

"Do you have the ring?" she asked, when she was settled on the ground again.

Parta nodded. "Then give it here," she said. Pulling the ring from his finger, he started to hand it to her when he noticed everything changing. First the color seemed to drain from the landscape, and a thin fog began to veil the scene. The scents vanished, and in their place the same hay fever that had plagued him since a child clogged once more his nose. The birdsong grew listless and ceased. He was about to put on the ring again, when he remembered his Quest. Already it seemed that he had wasted a lifetime in Now Land.

The old woman took the ring and then returned it to him, wrapped in blue paper. On the paper was another riddle.

> "There is a tunnel of many a turning,
> Within it lies the second, or Mercury ring,
> Within its darkness, the ring will glisten,
> With it you hear, if you but listen."

Parta read it twice, then stuffed it in his pocket. "No more tunneling in the earth for me," he said.

The old woman cackled at his remark, and leaping into the well, disappeared again.

Parta sat down and read the riddle aloud, hoping that the serpent would help him again. A cave or labyrinth of some kind was involved, he was sure, and for that he would need the serpent.

"I cannot help you further," said the serpent sadly. "Now you must go your way alone once more. But you must wear each ring that you win, else your sister is lost."

"But this leaden ring weighs me down in Now Land," said the Prince, "and makes me forget all purpose; indeed, I even regret leaving Now Land."

"While you wear the ring, Now Land will always be with you, for you carry it with you with the ring. So go now on your journey, and blessings be upon you."

The Prince stifled an urge to kiss the serpent's mouth, instead gazed intently into the eyes, and then stroking the head for luck, made off to the South.

He had walked on for most of the day when the ring made him full of sleep. Lying down in a clover meadow, he fashioned a clover ring for his right hand, while the leaden ring graced his left hand.

When he awakened, he saw a gigantic bird wearing spectacles standing over him, evidently about to try a bite of him.

"Now how's that for bad luck!" said the bird. "I find my first decent meal in two days and he proves to be not dead but sleeping. *Quad illicit eratum!* That means, what rotten luck."

"Very sorry that I'm not dead, I mean, for your sake," said Parta, jumping up in case the bird should change his mind.

"My name is Parta, and I'm a Prince, and I'm looking for my sister. Can you help me?"

"I am—with great regret—unable to help you. I have never seen a princess in these parts even from afar. Do me the honor of shaking claws. I am Howard, although most refer to me as Old Baldy."

"Why is that?" said the Prince. "You seem to have ample hair."

"Well, I wear a toupee," said Howard, doffing it like a cap. "Underneath I'm quite bald, but you see, I'm supposed to be—I'm an eagle. My wings are full of buckshot holes, and I've lost half my feathers, but I've survived so long because my senses are keen. *Sensorium keenum solong.* I can see twenty miles with my cheaters on, hear ten, and can smell them when the salmon rise to the top of the river. I'd invite you home to dinner, but you're probably vegetarian—so many of the young are these days. Where were you planning to spend the night?"

"Well, I hadn't thought about it," said Parta, "but this field of clover should make a jolly good bed."

"You couldn't sleep here—there's trolls about after dark!"

"Oh, what shall I do?" said Parta.

"Why don't you fly up to my nest with me, and in the morning we'll use my keen senses to look for your princess."

"Does the nest shake in wind? I'm afraid of heights."

"Not at all. *Non shakum windum.* My humble home lies on a mountain top."

"Then I shall be glad to accept your kind offer, Howard Baldy."

"Just Howard or Baldy, but not together if you please . . . Cleared for take-off are we?" said Howard, putting on a leather flying cap with goggles. "Then climb up on my back and we're off."

"Do you need those goggles to see while flying?" said Parta, mounting the eagle.

"No, but it helps to keep the cheaters on."

Take-off was rough, the eagle hopping along the ground until a slight downslope enabled him to lift into the air. Soon they were out over the river.

"Would you care for the fish dinner?" said Old Baldy, skimming the surface. Dropping suddenly, and reaching down with his talons, he clasped a fat salmon. The added weight made him flap harder to gain altitude. "Lord, this is hard work for an old bird like me."

Gradually they gained altitude ascending in long circular flight. It was nearly totally dark when they alighted on the side of a mountain, surmounted by two gigantic boulders. The evening star was the first to greet them.

"Star bright, star bright, first star I see tonight, I wish I may, I wish I might, have the wish I wish tonight," said Parta.

"What is your wish?" said Howard.

"One can't tell, can one, else it doesn't come true."

"But one can guess, can't one," said Howard. *"Unum guessum princessum."*

Parta slept on a nest of pine boughs and dreamed of a beautiful woman all in white dancing in a fire, the flames leaping with her like dancing partners. In the morning, the first ray of the sun over a distant hill struck the nest and had Parta stirring. Old Baldy still slept with his head tucked under one gigantic wing. From his corner of the nest, Parta could look out on a vast panorama. Below was the river, a silver serpent meandering through the clover valley. In the distance, the serpent met the sea and became one with it. In the other direction, many miles away, Parta just could make out the well and garden where he had been.

Amazing what this ring does for the eyesight, he thought. With a little sadness he realized that his eyes were not yet keen enough to see the serpent, if, indeed, it still encircled the well.

Then, with a start, Parta remembered the riddle, for the eagle's nest was situated on the edge of a cave. Parta fished into his pocket and read again the blue paper.

> "There is a tunnel of many a turning,
> Within it lies the second, or Mercury ring,
> Within its darkness the ring will glisten,
> With it you hear, if you but listen."

When he had finished, he knew he had to explore this tunnel. The riddle proved true, for no sooner had he pushed his way through a thick tangle of underbrush near the entrance, then the tunnel turned sharply and began a gradual descent. After a while it became so dark that he had to crawl, and another sharp turn made him decide to abandon his exploration until he could bring in more light, when there in the dark gleamed a ring of phosphorescence.

"The ring of Mercury!" he cried aloud, clapping his hands in delight.

Just then there was a roar such as wild beasts in a jungle make when angered, and the tunnel shook, the ring winking out.

It's not a ring at all, feared Parta, but the eye of some great beast and I have stumbled into its lair.

"Mister Baldy, help me!" he cried.

Another roar from the beast or beasts followed his outcry, and the floor of the cave tilted, and from somewhere above light streamed into the tunnel. Again the ring appeared, and Parta could see that it was a ring and not an eye. He scurried forward and put it on his finger. Old Baldy was calling to him from above. As fast as his feet could carry him, he ran out of the cave.

When he had told Baldy of his adventure, he heard again the sound of roaring beasts.

"What is that?" he asked.

"I've never heard it before," said the eagle.

And then, gazing out over the valley, river, and the panorama below, Parta knew that the well was where he had been, and that the future lay ahead where the river met the sea. There was a grand pattern that he was a part of, that he was *creating*, and in which his sister would be discovered.

"The first ring weighed me down in the senses, but now I have a new perspective," he told the eagle. "But the riddle says something about hearing with the ring if I but listen." He put the ring to his ear and heard—nothing. Then he passed it to the eagle, and he heard—nothing.

All at once, their ears reverberated to the sound of the great beasts, only now they were two voices, speaking at once.

> "Now you have much more than sense,
> And as we two can tell you,
> Two heads are better than one
> But two are only half of four,
> To make you whole, you need two more."

"Who are you?" cried Parta.

"We are the sleeping giants, Twins, and quite alike, one body, this mountain, with two heads, sleeping a thousand years yet guarding the Mercury ring, awakened from our slumber by your talking in our ear."

"So!" said Parta, "The riddle fools! One hears with the tunnel of many turnings—the ear!"

"Had you the ring when first you read the riddle, you would not have been fooled, and now your thinking will be straighter," said the Twins.

"Goodbye, good giants," said Parta, "and return to slumber another thousand years. I go in search of the third ring."

So saying, he climbed upon the eagle's back, and they descended to the well like a thunderbolt striking from the sky. From his new perspective, Parta could clearly see the two-headed Twins, laughing and urging him on.

To Parta's disappointment, the serpent was not at the well. Just then the old crone stuck her head out of the well.

"You've done well," she said, "but the two most difficult tests lie ahead. I'll give you the green riddle next," which she took from her pocket. Parta read aloud:

"Let an odd fish serve you to find the silver.
When your stomach does its deepest thinking,
it lets you know by crabbing that it hasn't eaten,
You claim the ring by sinking, and being eaten."

"Howard," said Parta, "may I beg a last favor of you? Would you fly me to the sea, and there drop me off?"

BY THE BEAUTIFUL SEA

Intending to descend into the sea from a great height, Parta had missed the mark and landed in the river mouth, where he crawled out onto the bank to see a fish—of all things!—reclining. And what a strange creature. The fish had large blubbery lips like a jewfish, and wore tortoise-shell spectacles, and a formal dinner jacket, whilst smoking an elegant pipe.

"You appear to be a cod," said the Prince, "but can you give me a logical demonstration that you are to be trusted?"

"Of course, sir, said the fish, "some fish are not to be trusted—terrible cods. But allow me to present myself, Old Liver Lips is the name, a gentleman's gentleman, if I do say so myself, sir. But how can I be of service?"

"Well," said Parta, "I have a riddle."

"Of course you do, sir, of course you do. Don't they always? I mean, you must be a Prince—knowed it the moment you rode up—or swam up."

"How do you know I'm a Prince?"

"Well, it shows, don't it, sir? I mean royalty proves out. It's the breeding of course, good breeding can't be disguised. And Princes always carry a pack or two of good riddles to while the time away, because time does tend to drag in fairyland, don't it, sir? Looking for a girl, are you, sir? Say no more, say no more! They're always chasing girls and looking for money. Just like the rest of us, eh?" said the fish, winking.

"Now look here, my man," said Parta irritatedly, "I'm not chasing girls, I'm questing a maiden, and she happens to be my sister."

"That's what they all say, sir, that's what they all say," and he laughed heartily. "Now I don't suppose she comes without a dowry, a *treasure* of some kind?"

"Well," said Parta, "if you must know it's a kingdom."

The fish laughed heartily again.

"But only a small kingdom," said Parta.

"Say no more, say no more," said Old Liver Lips. "Let's have a go at your riddle. Certainly the kernel of meaning will crack for logic."

"Very well," said Parta, "That sounds logical enough. The first line is, 'Let an odd fish serve you to find the silver.' "

"Well, I ask you," said Old Liver Lips, "what could be more explicit. Obviously I am to serve you."

"Don't go jumping to illogical conclusions," said Parta, logically. "The line says an *odd* fish must be in my service."

"Right you are, right you are, sir! But I ask you now, how many fish have you seen lolling about on river banks?!"

"Why none, now that you mention it."

"Stands to reason, then, don't it, that I am the odd fish what got throwed back, only they didn't quite get me back."

"You are odd, I'll admit that," said Parta.

"A fish out of water is not worth his salt, so throw me back and I'll be eternally grateful to Your Grace."

"Not so fast," said Parta. "How do I know that you won't just swim off?"

"Well, you don't sir. I suppose that's why you're looking for another ring.

"*Touché,*" said Parta. "But how did you know I was looking for a ring?"

"The riddle says so, doesn't it, sir? And anyhow, we fairyland folk know more than we're supposed to. That's because we're never what we seem."

"I see," said Parta. "Before, with just the leaden ring, I was stuck in my senses and could only go by what they told me. So it was easy to be tricked by appearances. Now since I have this mercury ring, I'm ever so much more rational."

"I'm appealing to your *reason* now, I am," said Liver Lips. "You've read fairy stories before. Isn't everyone under some kind of enchantment? I mean, how many fishes actually talk, sir?"

"Quite right," said the Prince. "Then you'll do me the honor of telling me who you really are, and why they left you like a fish out of water?"

"Hold on, hold on. If I told you that, this story would be over, and all the readers cheated out of a marvellous little tale that the author's got us in, if I don't mind saying so myself."

"It is rather good, isn't it," said Parta, importantly.
"Play the game, play the game, sir, that's the spirit."
"All right, let's get on with it then." So saying, he hoisted up the fish in his arms and tossed him between two banks. Presently there came a groan.
"I'm afraid you missed, sir!"
"How's that?"
"Well, you tossed me between two banks, but the river lies between those two banks over there."
With another mighty heave, the Prince found the right banks this time and deposited Old Liver Lips back in his native element.
"It's nice to be back in my native element. Oh, sorry, I didn't realize The Narrator had said that already."
"I'll thank you not to read my lines," said The Narrator peevishly.
"Look," said Parta. "The Narrator can't have any lines of dialogue; otherwise he's not the narrator anymore, and then who can narrate the story? I certainly can't. I'm the Prince and I've got enough to do trying to solve these foolish riddles that The Author has written into the story."
"Wait just a darn minute!" said The Author. "I'm not going to sit here and stand for the characters commenting on my lines. Since when do they become critics? This certainly wouldn't have happened in the old-time fairy tales. The characters knew their place then."
"I was just going to say, sir," said Liver Lips, "you get no respect anymore."
"Look!" cried Parta to The Author, "You and The Narrator have got into the story and there's no one to write it anymore. Now I'm going to count ten, and when I get to the next paragraph I don't want to see any of you anymore!"
"Thank God for that," said Parta, alone in the next paragraph. "Would you send back the fish? When I said everyone get out, I didn't mean the bona fide characters."
With a splash, the fish landed between the right two banks and the story—like the river—meandered on.
"Whew!" said Liver Lips, cleaning his glasses. "First I'm thrown out by two fishermen, then the hero dumps me between the wrong two banks, then I'm thrown out of the story, and now I'm back in the river again. It's been quite a day, I can tell you, sir."

"Can we get on with it?" said The Publisher.

"Straight away!" said everyone, snapping to.

"You see," said the Prince, "that's what too much logic does for you. You fall into its opposite and things start getting crazy."

"Well, sir," said Old Liver Lips, "if you don't mind me saying so, I think you've forgotten completely about the Princess."

"How could I forget?!" said the Prince, playing it straight. "I carry her image always in my heart."

"If I may be of service, sir," said Liver Lips, "you've been down in the ground and up in the air, and that leaves only one more place to go, doesn't it?"

"That's logical," said Parta.

"And you'll 'find the ring by sinking,' according to the riddle, so climb up on my back and I'll take you down to the bottom of the sea."

"I'll drown!" cried Parta.

"Not in fairyland you won't, sir. Not even a proper wetting for a fish like myself."

Well, our weird travelers had been swimming a very long time when they came to a sign that said *Welcome to the Bottom of the Sea. Trespassers Will Be Eaten.*

"End of the line!" shouted Liver Lips. "Everybody off!"

Parta slid from the fish's back and landed on the sand.

"Thank you, dear friend, I surely did not drown, and this—if we can believe our senses—is the bottom of the sea."

"Indeed it is, sir, and none too hospitable a bottom, if we can believe that sign."

"Now, dear friend, we must take our leave, for the next step in the journey is to come."

"And what might that be, sir?!" said Liver Lips, wondering where the Prince might stroll to.

"Well," said Parta, "the last line says I'll find the ring by 'sinking and being eaten,' so it's clear enough, you've got to eat me."

"What, me, sir?" said the cod, taken aback. "No offense meant, but you're not my cup of tea."

"I know," said the Prince, stamping his foot impatiently in the sand until a big cloud swirled about them, "you have to do what I say. I need the next ring to help me find the Princess."

"I'm sorry, sir, but I just couldn't get you down. I'm sure there's some of you feels the same way about eating cod, so I hope you'll understand, sir."

"I don't want to play the role of the Bad Prince and you're making me do it. The riddle says I'm to be eaten, so the sooner you can accommodate me the better."

"With all due respect to logic, sir, it is clear you are to be eaten, but by whom or what it does not say."

"That's just it! There's no one else around to do the job, and if you don't get on with it soon, I'll surely starve to death, for my stomach is grumbling its malcontent."

The thing is, sir, in fairyland, when people go about saying they are to be eaten, it doesn't take very long for someone or something to want to oblige them. And if you'll look to your left just a little, you may notice an eye watching you."

"An eye!" The Prince nearly jumped out of his skin.

"An eye, sir. And by the looks of it, it's on a swivel, because it looks at me, and then it looks at you."

Sure enough, just a few steps away there was what appeared to be an old stalk growing out of the sand, but at the top of the stalk was a turgid eye that moved its glance from one to the other as they spoke. Presently a great cloud of sand rose up, and a giant crustacean rose out of the sand. Tucking up a fiddle under his chin, he proceeded to play a merry dance for our travelers.

"Silliest thing I've ever seen," said the Prince, "a crab playing the violin."

"Not silly at all," said the crab. "I'm a fiddler."

"He's got you there," laughed the fish. "Hoisted on your own petard of logic."

"Come with me," said the crab, "to the palace of the King Crab, there to be part of a great feast."

"Oh, goodies," cried the Prince. "I'm famished."

They hadn't gone very far, when the sound of crabbing was unmistakable. "Can't get decent servants these days," came the voice. "All run off to find princesses or treasure!"

The King Crab was a very great crab indeed, measuring twenty feet from tip to tip, and for complaining he was even grander.

"Well, what have we here?" He eyed the travelers suspiciously.

"Two poor wanderers, lost and near starving at the bottom of the sea," said the Prince.

"Hard cheese," said the King. "And here I am with a feast all prepared, hundreds of crabby guests, and no one to serve it, because my servants have all run off."

"That is *bad* news," said Old Liver Lips, "but logic has sent us to the right place."

"Logic?" said the crab.

"Yes, you see, Your Grace, I am a gentleman's gentleman, presently unemployed, and my friend here is looking to be a part of your feast."

The King Crab clapped his claws together in delight. "This is the best news I've had since crab prices dropped!"

The Prince kissed Liver Lips full on his fat lips and said, "Dear friend, now we must part, for the Crab shall surely devour me and I shall somehow find the ring of silver."

"A ring of silver?" said the Crab suspiciously.

"Yes, I require it to find my Princess, and I am to be eaten in the process."

"Well, I can't help you there," said the Crab. "I eat seafood, not junk food."

"But I am a prince," said Parta indignantly.

"Can't help that," said the Crab. "I can tell by looking at you that your cholesterol count is too high for my old blood."

"Well then, have some of your servant crabs eat me," said the Prince.

"Not me," said the fiddler, turning up his feelers.

"I feel unwanted," said the Prince, starting to cry.

"It's no good going on like that," said Old Liver Lips, patting his shoulder with a fin. "You can come to the palace kitchen with me, and I shall serve the King."

THE PALACE

"I feel as if I've gone over to my inferior function," said the Prince, drying his tears.

"With all due respect, sir, you seem to have forgotten basic logic," said the fish, loading a gigantic silver tray with scallops, shrimp, and oysters. "Don't you think it a bit queer, sir, that the Crab don't want to eat you. I mean, everyone knows crabs eat anything!"

"That's right, they do!" said Parta.

"Well, sir, as I see it, I've got to serve you."

"And well you have, dear fish," cried Parta, unable to resist planting another kiss on his dear friend's liver lips.

"Stick to business," said Liver Lips. "What I mean is, he must have a very good reason for not wanting to eat you, and it must have something to do with the ring, or The Author wouldn't have written it this way. So when I say I must serve you, I refer to the riddle, 'Let an odd fish serve you to find the silver.' And by serve, I mean I must put you on this tray with the edibles so that the Crab *does* eat you."

"A capital idea!" rejoiced Parta.

"Then here, sir, slip on this shrimp's skin and nestle down amongst the mayonnaise, and before you know it, you'll be inside the King's stomach. Remember, I'll be watching for you when you come out. Take the back door, so to speak, and you'll arouse the least suspicion."

Peeking over a mountain of mayonnaise, the Prince in his shrimp suit began to have second thoughts about being eaten. Swallowed wasn't so bad, but first being torn to shreds by those gigantic claws was more than he could bear.

"Think of the Princess, and screw up your courage," said Liver Lips.

And just then, the giant claw moved to the shrimp and began to stuff them into his busy mouth, they being small enough to enter his gullet without rending.

Feeling only a small nip, the Prince slid down the King Crab's gullet, coming to rest inside of what felt like a silver barrel, but which he soon recognized to be the very ring he sought. Rolling it before him, he made for the back door. There was a long line there waiting to be expelled, so great was the Crab's feast, but the Prince, pulling rank, muscled his way to the fore. Just then he shot out, as through a giant trap door, and had not traveled far in the sea when Old Liver Lips, having swam around to the back, sucked him into his mouth and swam safely to the top.

"Ptooouuii," said the fish, spitting him out. "I must say that's offal."

Clutching the ring for dear life, the Prince now noticed that it had shrunk to his size, and bore a slender silver chain so that it could be worn about the neck. When he had put it on, he had a feeling that he had been wrong to ever doubt the fish. His senses and all the reason in the world could not tell him that in the way that he knew it all at once now.

THE WELL

Suddenly Parta was back with the old woman at the well. "You have succeeded so far, but one test yet remains."

"Enough, old woman," said the Prince. "I no longer doubt that you mean well. With this silver ring I know that you have only my well being at heart. Indeed, I feel that you labor now to disguise a certain love for me. But I must speak sincerely. I was betrothed at birth to the Princess that I quest, and no one can dissuade me from finding her."

"Tis well you are so faithful. I am sure your Princess will value highly this quality. Your journey is made to acquire the qualities that the rings do symbolize and confer. Now your brain and senses are balanced by a feeling in the gut that helps you make the right decisions. But one can be deceived by the senses, the brain, and one's own judgment. There is yet another way of perceiving that flies beyond what is known. This you will need to add to the other rings before the Princess can be claimed for your own."

"Give me then the last riddle," said Parta.

The old woman smiled at him. "It has few clues and many contradictions," she said, handing him the red riddle. Parta read:

> "Now you must choose the right.
> One is true and sees through all,
> The other false and gold of fools.
> Put on the right and see with second sight."

"Can you not tell me more?" lamented the Prince.

"Goodbye," called the crone, climbing into the well. "Follow the salamander wherever it leads you. There the last ring is forged."

THE FOUR-IN-ONE

Prince Parta had walked now three days and three nights before lying down at last to sleep. His slumber was troubled by the strange lands he had journeyed through and the

WELCOME TO THE BOTTOM OF THE SEA
TRESPASSERS WILL BE EATEN
E. GILL

wondrous sights he had seen, the King of Evil on his throne, the two-headed Twins, and the King Crab in his kingdom under the sea. Upon awakening, the Prince felt depressed.

"I have been into the earth, the sky, and the sea; there is nowhere else that she can be."

He was about to cry when he saw he was being watched by the strangest creature he had ever seen, its body covered with glittering blue scales like a fish. It stood on four brown stumpy legs, underpinned by four claws or talons each. Of varying shades of green, the head and tail resembled that of a serpent, only the eyes were red and saucer-like. But oddest of all were the gigantic yellow wings extruding from the sides of the blue scaly body.

"What creature are you?" asked Parta.

"I am the Fourth, the Four-in-One," it said.

"Another riddle!" said Parta delightfully. "But lead on and I'll follow."

They had walked many days and many nights, never stopping to rest, when in a dense forest, Parta slipped to his knees and could go on no longer.

"You must ride on my back," said the Four-in-One.

No sooner had Parta mounted then he fell into a deep sleep. Soon he was dreaming of his sister, who had been thrown into an oven by a witch, and now was calling his name to rescue her as the oven got hotter and hotter.

Parta awoke feeling the hot morning sun beaming directly on his face. His legs were astride the Four-in-One, and for a moment he was not sure where he was. Sitting up, he almost fainted with fear, for he was flying high in the sky, the creature's yellow wings slowly beating the air.

"Where are you taking me?" he cried.

Suddenly the giant reptilian head swung around and looked him directly in the eye. "Why, to the Princess, of course," came the reply.

Parta began to laugh. "Don't you get the impression, whilst flying forwards and looking backwards, that you're only staying in the same place?"

"It won't be long now," said the creature. "When we reach the sea and begin to dive, you must hold on tight, for we go to the bottom of the sea."

Soon the sea was in sight, a tiny ribbon of blue at the edge of the earth. Then they began a long glide that ended in a dive to the sea floor.

"End of the line," said Four-in-One, when they had touched the sand. "Now hold on to my tail. The castle is a short swim from here."

What an unusual sea, thought Parta, for people walked about on the bottom, just as if they never knew they were undersea. Here came a herdsman, followed by his cows and sheep, and there an itinerant juggler. Juggling is easy down here, thought Parta, the balls stay up so long. Fish swam about, passing in among the people.

Ahead lay a purple mountain, which they reached in an hour's time. Around the edge of the mountain wound a narrow path, just wide enough for the Four-in-One with its wings folded. Parta followed behind. Seven times they circled the mountain. At the top there stood a castle which Parta was sure was not there when they were approaching the mountain—nor even there when they were ascending.

At the gate they stopped. "Now you must ask permission to enter," said the Four-in-One, stepping aside. Parta boldly knocked; the gate flew open.

An old man stood before them. He leaned heavily on a staff, the other hand carried a lantern in which blue and red flames glowed, commingling. His white beard fell nearly to his feet, and over his eyes he wore the most curious goggles, star-shaped and purple in color.

"I am Princess Parta, come in search of my lost sister, who the King, my father, has said shall be my bride . . . Are you the king of this castle?"

"No," smiled the old man. "I am not the king. The king is in the pot, cooking."

What a strange supper we shall have, thought Parta.

They followed the old man into a great courtyard, in the middle of which was a square enclosure. Ahead lay a huge door, all of lead, engraved with this sign: ♄

Stopping before the door, the ancient man turned to Parta, holding out his hands, "The door of lead opens only to the ring of lead." Parta drew back, afraid this was some ruse to separate him from the hard-won ring of lead.

The Four-in-One turned its head and peered back at Parta. "You must comply, else she is lost."

Parta held out his hand, and the Ancient One slipped it

from his finger. Carefully inserting it into a hole in the door, in which it perfectly fit, he turned the ring. Immediately there was a great creakng and groaning from the door. Ponderously it began to slowly open. they were now in a room of such pitch blackness that even the lamp of the Ancient One threw no light, but was stifled in its glass, and made only a poor beacon which the two travelers followed for what seemed a very long time.

Ahead in the black was another door, shimmering as if it were not solid but a dancing will-of-the-wisp. When they had reached it, Parts saw that it bore this sign: ☿

"This door is made of mercury," said the old man. "May I have your ring?"

Parta hesitated only a moment, then gave over the mercury ring from his left hand. When placed in the hole made for it, it caused the door to fly open silently as if upon a spring.

The room which they now entered enclosed a ballet of dancing lights and colors, much like the fireworks Parta had seen from his own castle parapet on occasions of great pomp and circumstance.

"These are the neurons," said the Ancient One.

Parta would have stayed there forever, so wondrous was their display, but the Four-in-One prodded him onward with its head, as a sheepdog might its master, reluctant in the early morning to be about his flock.

Finally they came to another door, on which had been etched the sign of a half moon: ☽ The door was of silver and shone like the moon itself. When Parta's last ring had been given from next to his heart, the door proved not to be there at all, for what had seemed to be silver was in reality moonlight, and they stepped through it like a silver waterfall.

All around them on the ground lay humans and creatures fast asleep. The strangest of creatures were evidently shapes of nightmares, for they hovered about the heads of the sleeping persons and did not sleep themselves.

When they came to where she was lying, a beautiful woman awoke and stood before the old man. Her beautiful black hair fell to her waist, and she was engirdled with a chain of silver moons.

"All is in readiness," she whispered to the Ancient One. "I have dreamed everything."

Then they followed her to another square courtyard, which they never entered through any door, but which was at once around them. In the center on the ground were drawn two trines, their points facing in opposite directions so that together they made a six-pointed star. Heaped upon this symbol were logs, crossed for burning. Suspended over the logs—he knew not how—was a giant glass chamber, round, and tapered at the top.

Now Parta could see that there were four doors in the courtyard, three of which bore the insignia of the doors through which they had entered; yet Parta remembered that the three doors had been in succession, and they had not entered *this* courtyard, so how could it be around him now, he wondered?

The Ancient One now spoke. "There is no exit from the oven except by the golden door." And Parta now saw that this door was emblazoned with the sun's majestic symbol: ⊙

The Ancient One and the woman carried a ladder to the side of the crucible, erecting it against the glass side. The Ancient One then asked Parta again for his three rings, explaining, "They are to be sacrificed in the fire." At this Parta drew back, not wishing to risk the loss of the rings that had brought him so far in his Quest.

"You must willingly give them up," said the Four-in-One, "else all is lost."

"Willingly do I then," said Parta, giving them to the Ancient One.

Opening his cape, he revealed a sword, the hilt forged of metal, but the blade glittered like diamonds. This he exchanged for Parta's three rings, which he enfolded in his cape, then climbed the ladder to the opening at the crucible's top. "All is ready," he said.

In the side of the crucible was a door, imperceptible to the eye, which the woman now opened, indicating that Parta enter, followed by the Four-in-One. Carrying his sword, he stepped in. The door closed behind them.

"Light the fire," said the Ancient One, peering down at them.

Soon the glass began to moisten with steam from the

solution in the bottom of the crucible. Distillates formed just above the line of liquids. The steam and fog thickened.

"Stand back," cried the old man, and he hurled down black powders which burst into fire when they settled into the liquid below. A black smoke engulfed Parta and the Four-in-One. "Now the ring of lead goes in," called out the Ancient One.

As he watched, Parta saw the smoke part briefly and through it there gleamed the eyes of the King of Evil himself, from whom Parta had won the ring of lead. Again the black smoke and mist closed and he saw in it serpents writhing. When it had parted again, there were his two brothers in chains around the King of Evil.

The smoke and mist began to clear and he could hear the Ancient One chanting:

"As dark begins to lighten,
When king is ripe and old,
Then his beard and head whiten,
And all shall turn to gold."

Parta then saw a figure sitting in the liquid in the bottom, as one might in his Saturday night bath. The skin was black as soot, and the hair and beard were white as snow, but it was no longer the King of Evil, but a Moor of kingly mien, and as he sat and sweated in his bath, the crown of his head whitened further until it became gleaming gold.

Now, from above, more powders descended to burst into flame, raising mists and smokes of multi-colored hues. Out of this a new figure rose as the old man called out, "Freely given, the ring of mercury goes in."

One body with two heads, one black, one white, and one half the body black, the other white, one head laughing foolishly, evil in appearance, and ugly to gaze upon, the other head, wisely silent, fair and benign in countenance. The black head was that of a man; the white head was a woman fair.

From above came the Ancient One's chant:

"When two comes as one androgyne,
Then Four-in-One is not far behind."

This apparition now dissipated and fresh powders fell from the cape of the Ancient One. The crucible was becoming unbearably hot, and Parta began to shed his clothes.

"Now finally, the silver ring, given as great sacrifice, goes in."

At this a blue mist commenced to coalesce at the center of the crucible. From this mist the body of a woman formed. Beautiful to behold, her waist was encircled by a silver chain. Her skin was milky like the moon at the full. Fire leaped up around her feet; yet she moved not nor cried out. Above the crackling flames, the Ancient One chanted:

"The white virgin must truly wed
The blind but fearsome lion of red.
His eyes will only fill with sight,
When he has devoured the woman white."

The woman now began to dance in the fire. Four-in-One turned its head to Parta and spoke for the first time since they had entered the crucible.

"Follow me into the fire and watch me redden."

"I shall burn," said the Prince, "and my reason says I must not go into the fire. But my feeling says that you are to be trusted and I must follow."

"I live in earth, air, and water, and in the fourth where lives no other."

The Four-in-One entered the fire, and immediately its wings opened and embraced the flames. Within moments the creature's wings had volatilized and no wings now remained. The fishlike scales on its body began to hiss and pop, losing their moisture to the inexorable power of the flames. As the scales shriveled and blackened, peeling away from the flesh beneath, where flesh was exposed the blood gushed forth and ran down its body, which now turned crimson throughout. The creature reared up on its hind legs, wriggling this way and that in the flames, and now Parta realized that without its wings and scales it resembled a giant salamander.

As the white woman danced, the Ancient One now threw down powders of fiery red, upon which the flames fed and leaped up the sides of the crucible. Out of these flames a new creature began to take shape. At first it was indistinguishable from the flames, but then a wreath of fire became a red mane, and in the center of this mane the head of a great red lion appeared, but with empty sockets where eyes should be.

E. GILL

The lion walked about the crucible, following each scent, finally coming to Parta, who cringed at the very edge of the crucible. With his great muzzle, he nudged Parta towards the center where the fire was hottest and the flames leaped ever high. In desperation, Parta looked up appealingly to the old man on his ladder.

"Fear not," he said, "the Four-in-One will save you in the fire."

But the Four-in-One seemily was all afire now, rayed in blood like the last beams of a fiery sunset. The lion reared up on its hind legs and opened its forward claws as if to maul Parta, and Parta, fearing the great beast, thrust out in front of him the sword, inverted, with the blade down and the hilt uppermost like a cross. The lion reared backwards into the fire. Now they were four in fire: white woman, red lion, salamander, and Parta, but the flames burned him not, and a temperate circle surrounded him.

It seemed now that the white woman and the Four-in-One danced in the fire, or that the flames followed their movements in arabesques of exotic colors as more powders rained down from the Ancient One's cape of plenty.

Around the white woman now an aura appeared of all the colors of the rainbow, and her face and raiment became as glorious as a goddess. She held out her arms to Parta, and entranced with this vision of ultimate beauty, he moved to accept her embrace. Before he could, her features changed, and he saw again the face of the aged crone at the well, and around her now the aura was trimmed with the darkness of hell, so that light and dark harmonized and entwined together in an exquisite dance of heaven and hell. The dark became ice and coated her from head to toe in the fire, and upon her head a crown of ice crystals sprouted, the crystals like gems of flame.

Most wondrously as he watched, the face of the crone and the face of the goddess phased in and out, now goddess, now crone, now beautiful, now ugly, now all goodness, now all evil.

The head of the Four-in-One swiveled on its long neck and spoke to him.

"Cut off her head *now,* and feed it to the red lion."

Parta was aghast. "I cannot!"

"Then all is lost."

"I do not know whether she is my beloved or my nemesis!" cried Parta.

The serpent head spoke now with wisdom, and Parta knew he must weigh what was said with his own new-found wisdom that the rings had bestowed.

"As long as she exists *without,*" said the serpent, "she is your projection. She can only marry with you *within* when she has ceased to exist without. Cut off her head and end the projection!"

Parta hesitated again, then knew what was true. Raising the sword, he struck a clean blow, the head severing just below the chin, the face caught in a phase of transformation from goddess to crone.

"Well done," said the serpent head, "and now one last task for you. Cut off my head."

"Dear friend," said Parta, "do not ask me that. Surely you did not bring me here to be your assassin."

"The fire grows cold, and gold sinks back to lead! Strike! And then feed both heads to the red lion!"

No sooner said than done, Parta now beheld the last marvel, for the hollow pits in the lion's head filled with two great rings of golden hue.

From overhead, at the same moment, came the ancient voice of the old man, reciting the last riddle.

> "Now you must choose the right.
> One is true and sees through all,
> The other false and gold of fools.
> Put on the right and see with second sight."

Parta stepped boldly up to the lion, peering into his two great eyes.

> "My senses tell me one is gold's true light.
> My mind tells me the riddle says the right.
> My feeling says that is not false but true.
> So I select not left but right."

As Parta plucked out the right eye of the lion, it surrounded his wrist like a golden bracelet. At once the flames leaped up around him, consuming the bodies of the salamander and white woman, and then devouring the devourer himself, the great red lion exploding in a ball of fire which shot Parta up into the air and out of the top of the crucible.

As he lay on the ground recovering his senses, the great golden doors around the courtyard, on which was emblazoned the sign of the sun, opened, music struck up, a chorus sang, and a wedding party entered the square. Foremost was his father the King. Behind him came his two brothers, each with a bride fair to see, and on their hands, gold rings. The wedding party parted now, and one stood alone. He knew her to be his bride and sister, the one whom he had sought from the beginning.

The choir was singing, and oddly he recognized among them the familiar faces from his father's own court:

"Now all the riddles have been told,
And you have won the ring of gold.
Now your sleeping sister can awake,
The forces of evil and darkness shake.
For the final secret that you learn
Is that she slept deep inside of you,
While in the world for her you did yearn
With Four-in-One, now claim your bride so true."

He knelt before her, and on her finger he placed the gold ring, named Four-in-One, so newly won, forged from the rings of lead, mercury, and silver. He knew he was at last whole, and the ring could be freely given to his betrothed. She moved towards him, taking his spirit into her as he took her soul into himself.

She spoke. "I have always been with you, but in the darkest reaches of your soul where light and thoughts seldom penetrate. Your journey has been to the interior. No time of the world's time has passed, and you are still at your father's castle."

And sure enough it was true, for as more torch-bearers entered the courtyard, accompanied by musicians sounding trumpets and plucking lutes, this place, once stranger than strange, was none other than home.

When the procession had all piled in, and each had arranged himself in a circle about the Prince and Princess, the chorus sang once more:

"Now all opposites are resolved.
Man weds woman, cold weds hot,
Dry with moist, bitter with sweet,
Bound and free, innocent and wise,
Up with down, awake with sleep,

Light with dark, good with evil,
And so the One eternally,
Ever and ever is born again."

And as this last was sung, and the wedding party fell silent, a baby's laugh was heard, and all eyes turned to the center, where stood the glass-walled athanor. Within a babe was seen, laughing and cavorting within the flames and calling to Parta and the Princess, "Papa! Mama!"

Needless to say, they lived happily ever after.

Primer for "The Four Rings"

Yet another area of psychology to which C.G. Jung made a lasting contribution is that of the concept of the four functions. Again, as in the concept of animus and anima, far from being mystical, the concept of the four functions has great practical application, for every moment of our waking lives involves utilization of at least one of the four functions. The four functions are divided into two groups, one group for perceiving outer reality (sensation and intuition), the other group for evaluating (thinking and feeling) what has been received.

Jungians speak of a primary or superior function, which indicates the one of the four functions most frequently used by the individual, his trump suit, so-to-speak. Since frequent use of one excludes the other, the least-used function, one's weakest suit, is designated the inferior function. The other two functions then are used in an alternate mode, sometimes one, sometimes another. The following diagrams present four possible combinations for four persons, with the superior function at the top.

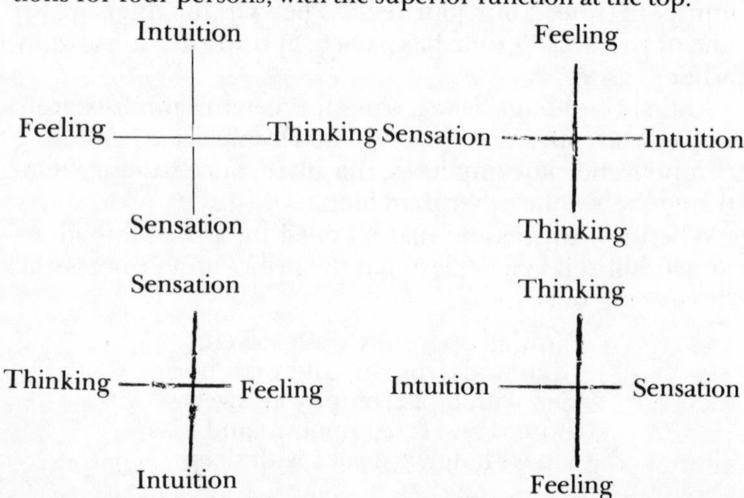

Again, the purpose of Jungian psychology is psychic wholeness, therefore, in order to be able to partially utilize the inferior function, we must work at it. But first we must know the superior function. Briefly, I shall summarize the functions. Sensation: perceiving by the five senses, you see, hear, taste, touch, and smell things that go unnoticed by an intuitive type. (The word *type* stands for a person, defining him or her by superior function.) Intuition: the sensation world is partially "dialed out" by an intuitive type, in order that his intuitions, hunches, and *inner* observations about the world may come through. In conversation, for example, an intuitive type may be listening with his ears, but his mind is somewhere else, perhaps making a "leap" of intuition between something you have just said and something he has read. A person of inferior sensation has to work at waking up to the evidence of the senses, particularly since objects always seem to be getting lost around an intuitive type. C.G. Jung was evidently an intuitive type.

The last two evaluating functions, thinking and feeling, are ways of appraising the outer reality. A thinking type is just what it says, an intellectual, whereas the feeling type does not use the intellect but instead *feels*: I like or dislike, e.g., I feel threatened, ergo I dislike the person or situation. This function should not be confused, however, with emotional *feelings,* since it is an *evaluating,* rational process.

One's attitude towards time is a particularly valuable tool in determining one's superior and inferior functions. The sensation type lives in the present, enjoying the moment, whereas the intuitive lives in the future, focusing on potential possibilities. The feeling type has a tendency to live in the past, constantly re-evaluating persons and events that had affected him favorably or adversely. The thinking type balances past, present, and future, evaluating from a more objective perspective. No one of these types is a "better" type than any other; the problem is to partially integrate the inferior function into consciousness so that it can be utilized when appropriately needed.

In "The Four Rings" I have created a classic quest tale, invoking a prince and a king, three brothers, and a princess who is to be quested. In terms of Jungian psychology, the king may be likened to the Self, he sets the task that will lead to individuation and living happily ever after. But the three sons pose a problem, since the three seek the fourth, four being the number of wholeness and completion: four directions, four elements, four functions, etc. Three brothers often turn up in folktales in which a treasure or maiden is sought, and in our tale the bride/kingdom/riches prize of wholeness is personified by a step-sister princess, who represents the fourth, or feminine principle excluded from consciousness. Indeed, Jung tells us many times that the anima personifies the inferior function. Thus, she must be found and restored to consciousness (awakened).

The youngest prince, Parta, reasons that she is to be found in the south, since the enchantment was laid by Queen Darkness, Witch of the South. South, or down, is the direction of the unconscious, where the anima/bride must reside, so the prince has reasoned or intuited correctly. But not only is the prince's direction South, he also must descend: the floor of a valley, a well, and the very bottom of the sea.

Parta's first encounter with the feminine principle is in the form of an old witch, but he has the proper response to her and wisely does not alienate her. In this encounter he must leave reason, since she tells him "only a fool would drink from this well." His reply, "In that case, it is folly to be wise," is an inspired intuition.

Next he encounters the serpent, another dangerous anima aspect, but the serpent has "soft brown eyes like a human being" that belie the danger. The serpent carries him through the element earth where in answer to the riddle the lead ring is found under the tongue of the Goat-Serpent, who speaks to Parta that the ring shall "free and bind" him at the same time. Here I have associated the element earth with the astrological sign of Capricorn, depicted as a mer-goat, ruled by the planet Saturn, the metallic equivalent for which is lead.

Now Land, a metaphor of the sensation function, where one lives in the present totally immersed in the five senses, nearly makes the Prince forget his Quest, "for here one cares not for the past, nor is concerned with the future." Ah, but think, dear reader, how difficult it would be to intuit anything about our universe, to formulate but one philosophical concept, if we had not five but twenty-five senses. Somewhere in the universe there may be just such life forms, and they must enjoy life very much, but they probably have no intuitions of us as we do of them.

Parta has learned from the serpent that four rings are involved in his Quest, but that "their magic works only when they are together." Each ring will confer the power of that function which it symbolizes, and together will bring him psychic wholeness.

Having acquired the ring of lead, Parta acquires his next magic helper, Howard, the bald eagle, who wears a toupee and has of course very keen senses. Inside the giant Twins' ear he finds the ring of mercury, which confers the power of the thinking function, associated with the element Air, the sign Gemini, the planet Mercury, and the metal mercury. Parta has now, two rings, two functions, and two more to acquire.

His next magic helper, Old Liver Lips, the fish is quite logical: "'If I may be of service, sir,' said Liver Lips, 'you've been down in the ground and up in the air, and that leaves only one more place to go, doesn't it?'"

Obligingly the fish guides Parta to the bottom of the sea: the element water, the sign Cancer, the crab, ruled by the moon, associated with the silver ring. Acquisition of the silver ring grants Parta the power of the feeling function. "When he had put it on, he had a feeling that he had been wrong to ever doubt the fish. His senses and all the reason in the world could not tell him that in the way that he knew it all at once now."

The last magic helper, the salamander Four-in-One, incorporates in one body lion, fish, bird, and serpent, that is to say, like the philosopher's stone of alchemy, the figure symbolizes the resolution of opposites. The four rings open four doors, the last made of gold, and now Parta must enter the last element—fire. But his magic helper stands him in good stead here, since according to alchemical tradition, salamanders were thought to live in fire. Our tale now takes an alchemical turn, with a crucible and the Ancient One (Key IX of the Tarot cards) who chants: "The white virgin must truly wed/The blind but fearsome lion of red." The white virgin and the red lion appear in Key VIII, Strength, of the Tarot cards, and the strength is that which comes from the resolution of opposites. The transmutation of lead into gold occurs in the crucible, and Parta acquires the last ring of intuition, associated with the red lion, Leo, the planet Sun, the element fire, and the metal gold.

At the tale's climax, there is a sacred marriage, or *hieros-gamos*, of Parta and his anima, the awakened princess. Parta has attained Selfhood, his Quest is complete. He had sought her without, but all along she had been within. Now she is resurrected from the sleep of unconsciousness, and is his equal partner in the Great Work that—"all opposites resolved"—has created the One again, the homunculus, or babe cavorting in the flames.

And, finally, to conclude, I should like to share with the reader a Big Dream which occurred at the beginning of my friendship with Joseph Campbell. In the dream, we are in a laboratory engaged in the Great Work. With us is another man, somewhat shadowy and of lesser significance. What is missing, as at the beginning of my tale "The Four Rings," is the fourth, or inferior function, which completes the quaternity. Three seeks resolution, and it is not long before we three are forced for economic reasons to take a fourth into the laboratory, a young boy whom we shall tutor. However, he is an immediate discipline problem, and I tell his grandmother I am going to kick him out of class. The classroom, of course, represents consciousness. As a personification of the inferior function, the boy had already been in the darkness of unconsciousness. Small wonder, then, that he is unadaptable now. An "undisciplined" sensation function signifies one who is not observant of external reality, since I am an intuitive type. Joseph Campbell probably represented the thinking function to me at that stage in my life, although I now know that he is an intuitive type. Our third colleague in the laboratory, somewhat less differentiated in appearance and playing a lesser role, was undoubtedly my feeling function.

Now Jung has said that the anima often personifies the inferior function. It is at this stage in the dream that she commences her *compensatory* role to consciousness. That is, our Great Work has involved highly rational processes, intuition and thinking collaborating with the intellectual judging function, feeling.

But she tells us, if we "kick her grandson out of the class," she will drive us out of the classroom, that is, out of our minds. Insanity and the unconscious fourth function, oppose rationality and consciousness. Her appearance now becomes like that of a witch; yet we tell her that nothing can dissuade us from our purpose to accomplish the Great Work. We go about our business, but suddenly in the air before our very eyes, a tangle of writhing vipers appears. We are forced out of the classroom.

In the dream's next stage, I learn her terms. She presents a small tree in a pot, hanging from which there is a single almond. I am told I must eat the almond. Recognizing the parallel of this tree to mythology, and fearing that I may be poisoned; nevertheless, I eat and become as if dead. There is a descent to the underworld (the unconscious) in a car, and then, as if resurrected, I sit up and am able to drive the car as the dream ends.

The anima has initiated a test or trial that has caused high and mighty consciousness to lower itself and become subservient to the dark powers of the unconscious. As in Prince Parta's initiation, he is forced to act in a way which defies reason in order to accomplish the purpose of wholeness. The *hierosgamos,* or sacred marriage, is a wedding of conscious and unconscious, light and darkness, reason and unreason, and a harmonizing of all pairs of opposites which we can name. Individuation, the goal of Jungian psychology seeks nothing less than that, and therefore, its importance transcends psychology and elevates it to philosophy. For some psychologists, this so-called mystical tendency of Jungian psychology is a violation of the *rational* ethic of psychology as a science; yet psychoanalysis is also a *healing* art, and as Jungian psychology—and my dream!—so clearly demonstrate, healing cannot be accomplished without the wholeness which is the marriage of conscious and unconscious.

And now, our journey is complete. We have entered the Dream Castle, descended into wells to reach the unconscious, soared in the sky on the back of an eagle, and even were swallowed at the bottom of the sea. We have juggled *personae* like masks at carnival, and having met the shadow, found he could be friend. Through the power of projection, we have fallen in love with frog princesses, and taking a trip on active imagination, we have followed a flute note to infinity. Finally, we have awakened to the world again only to find that all along we had been at home in our own Dream Castle, and that no time of the world's time has passed, and our journey has been to the interior.